★ The Way to U.S. ★
CITIZENSHIP

Margaret W. Hirschy
Patricia L. Hirschy

Reviewer
Maria Viramontes de Marin, Ph.D.

Dormac, Inc.

Executive Editor: Carlos A. Byfield
Copy Editor: Becky Colgan
Designer: Jana Whitney
Cover Designer: Carol Elwood Graphic Design
Typographers: Total Graphics, Inc.

 Dormac, Inc.
P.O. Box 270459
San Diego, California 92128-0983

ISBN 0-86575-657-0
Printed in U.S.A.

Contents

National Holidays and Symbols

Washington D.C.

State and Local Government

Immigration and Naturalization

California Government

The New President

Appendices

Introduction

The Way to U.S. Citizenship is a basic United States history and government workbook designed specifically for teaching ESL learners. It integrates two areas: **language** and **content.** Content and language are made more comprehensible to beginning and intermediate ESL learners by using proven pedagogical and linguistic devices to shelter the English language. The unique learning needs of the amnesty and citizenship candidates have been recognized.

The Way to U.S. Citizenship acknowledges that amnesty and citizenship candidates first need to be able to use language to pass required tests, as indicated by the INS. Later, they will need English to survive in an English-language setting. This text addresses fundamentally the primary need, without neglecting the other. Amnesty learners must first become permanent residents before they can apply for citizenship. This text includes the **IRCA Competencies,** designed by CASAS to help learners fulfill the necessary requirements to become residents and citizens.

The Way to U.S. Citizenship provides learners with the knowledge and understanding of history and government of the United States that they need initially. Often, knowledge and understanding occur first on the comprehension level before students are able to produce. The **Activity Section** of each lesson presents comprehension and production exercises. The skills that are necessary to cope with the learner's present needs are immediately focused in the appropriate contexts.

The Way to U.S. Citizenship also recognizes the need for practice and repetition and for communication by means of dialogue. Learners work individually, in pairs, and in groups, thus acquiring the exchange of meaningful content information as well as the structures needed to comprehend and give information.

Finally, **The Way to U.S. Citizenship** acknowledges that adult learners have acquired and use their native language for various purposes daily. It also recognizes that a lack of knowledge of English is **not** synonymous with ignorance and that what learners already know in their native language may be used as a device to help them learn/acquire a second language. This text incorporates many of these tools.

To the Teacher

The Way to U.S. Citizenship includes features that teachers have requested for many years.

- It integrates language and content— Learners are provided with practice exercises that encompass both aspects.
- It makes abundant use of **true cognates** — Learners can recognize words that in their native language are similar in form and meaning to words in English. This facilitates comprehension.
- It uses structures that are more parallel to those in the learners' native language — Content is easier to grasp.
- It makes abundant use of structures in the active voice — Content is easier to understand.

- It provides practice with communicative structures — Learners acquire pertinent language practice.
- It provides useful appendices, which include a glossary of English-Spanish terms — Learners can use their knowledge of the first language to help them learn/acquire the second language.

Structure of the Workbook

The Way to U.S. Citizenship contains 36 lessons. Each lesson lists the respective civic competencies. This list of competencies is followed by a narrative, an activity section with various exercises, and a quiz.

Terms or expressions perceived to be difficult for learners are italicized, and the equivalent term as used in that particular context is provided in Spanish in Appendix 8. The teacher's task has been made easier, yet at the same time the content has been sheltered as much as possible to minimize the learner's apprehension and to facilitate his/her comprehension of the content.

An answer key is provided, which allows learners to work at home or in a classroom setting.

Presentation of the Material

The reading passage in each lesson provides content in a sheltered manner; however, students need to be prepared for oral-aural interaction.

As the instructor, you must present the material. It is suggested that you provide some simple practice with listening exercises before reading. Ask questions to which students may respond with one-word answers — true, false, give a number, give a date, give a name — or by raising one or several fingers. Once the reading passage has been introduced, give practice with the material. Practice different ways questions are asked:

Q. What is the highest law of the land?
A. The Constitution.
Q. What is the Constitution?
A. The highest law of the land.
Q. Who was the first President?
A. George Washington.
Q. Who was George Washington?
A. The first President.
Q. How long is a senator's term?
A. Six years.
Q. How long does a senator serve?
A. Six years.

Say true or false.
A. Cuomo is the governor of California.
B. False.
A. Cuomo is the governor of New York.
B. True.

Read a sentence and have students give the respective Wh-word for the question.
A. Ronald Reagan was the President.
B. Who?
A. The new President took office in 1989.
B. When?

Give group practice and assignments. Have one group obtain from another the information each does not have. Provide for individual, pair, and group work.

The Way to U.S. Citizenship provides a variety of exercises that will facilitate your already difficult task. It will help learners learn/acquire the language and content they need to become U.S. residents and, eventually, U.S. citizens.

Lesson 1
Maps and the World

Competency Objectives

After completing Lesson 1, students will be able to **(1)** identify common features of maps and **(2)** locate the United States on a map.

There are many kinds of maps. They show the *surface* of the earth. Some maps show countries. Some maps show states. Other maps show cities, mountains, and large areas of water.

A globe is one kind of map. It is a round map that shows the *whole* surface of the earth. The North Pole is at the top of the globe. The South Pole is at the bottom of the globe.

A surface map is another kind of map. A surface map is a flat map that shows the whole world or just one part of it. Surface maps are usually on paper. The maps in this book are surface maps. The top of the surface map is north, and the bottom is south. The right side of the surface map is east, and the left side is west.

The equator is *halfway* between the North Pole and the South Pole. The equator runs through South America, Africa, and parts of Southeast Asia. The equator cuts the world into 2 hemispheres: the *Northern Hemisphere* and the *Southern Hemisphere*. The world is also divided into 2 other hemispheres: the *Eastern Hemisphere* and the *Western Hemisphere*. The United States is in the Northern and Western Hemispheres.

Maps of the world show the 7 continents on the surface of the earth. A continent is a very large area of land. The United States is on the continent of North America. The continent of North America also *includes* Canada and Mexico.

Maps of the world also show the 4 oceans. An ocean is a very large body of salt water. The United States is next to 2 oceans: the Atlantic Ocean and the Pacific Ocean.

Look at the map of the world in Appendix 1 and locate the United States on the map.

Activity Section

Activity 1
Match the two columns to complete each sentence.

1. A globe   _____ is west.

2. Most surface maps   _____ is the North Pole.

3. At the top of a globe   __1__ is a round map of the earth.

4. At the bottom of a globe   _____ is east.

5. The right side of a surface map   _____ are on paper.

6. The left side of a surface map   _____ is the South Pole.

Activity 2
Look at the map of the world in Appendix 1. Find the United States. Then answer these questions.

1. Which ocean is west of the United States?

_____

2. Which country is north of the United States?

_____

3. Which country is south of the United States?

_____

4. Which ocean is east of the United States?

_____

5. On which continent do you live?

_____

Activity 3 (pair or group work)
Ask a classmate the following questions. Then write the answers.

1. Which kinds of maps show the world?

_____

2. Where is the equator?

_____

3. Is a surface map round?

_____

4. How many hemispheres are there?

_____

5. How are surface maps and globes different?

_____

6. Are there 6 oceans in the world?

_____

7. Which hemisphere is the United States in?

_____

8. Which continent is the United States on?

_____

Quiz

Choose words from the box. Fill in the blanks to complete each sentence.

continents	globe	equator
oceans	Atlantic Ocean	pole
continent	south	

1. There are 7 _____ in the world.

2. A _____ shows the whole surface of the earth.

3. The _____ is a large body of water next to the U.S.

4. The bottom of a surface map is _____.

5. The _____ is halfway between the North Pole and the South Pole.

6. There are 4 _____ in the world.

7. The United States is on the _____ of North America.

Lesson 2
Columbus and the Native Americans

Competency Objectives
After completing Lesson 2, students will be able to **(1)** identify Columbus as the person who discovered America, **(2)** state the date Columbus discovered America, **(3)** identify the original inhabitants of the U.S., and **(4)** describe how the inhabitants lived.

Christopher Columbus was born in Genoa, Italy. He was a navigator. He sailed far north to England and far south to the Azores. He thought there was a shorter way to India if he crossed the Atlantic. Columbus studied the winds and currents of the ocean. He went to the king and queen of Spain with his ideas. They helped him.

In 1492, Christopher Columbus found the land we call America. Columbus wanted to find a shorter way to the Indies. The *king* and queen of Spain gave Columbus 3 ships for the trip. Columbus sailed west across the ocean until he came to land. Because he *thought* the land was the Indies, he called the people living there "Indians." Columbus was not in the Indies. He had found a land new to Europeans.

There were different groups of Indians. Each had different customs and languages. Some were *hunters*. Some were *fishermen* or *farmers*. The groups, or nations, had different kinds of houses and leaders. All of the nations took care of the land. They took from the land only what they needed.

Today we call the Indians "native Americans" because they were the first people to live on the North American continent.

Activity Section

Activity 1
Match the two columns to complete each sentence.

1. Before 1492, Europeans   _____ native Americans.

2. Christopher Columbus sailed   _____ Indians.

3. The king and queen of Spain   _____ different customs.

4. Columbus called the people living in America   _1_ did not know about America.

5. Another name for Indians is   _____ west until he saw land.

6. The different nations had   _____ a shorter way to the Indies.

7. Columbus wanted to find   _____ gave Columbus 3 ships.

Activity 2
Complete these sentences.

The name of the man who found America is _____.

The king and queen of _____ gave him ships to go to

the Indies. In the year _____, he sailed _____ and

found a new land. The people in the new land lived in groups called

_____. We now call those people _____

because they were the first people to live on the continent of

_____.

Activity 3
Practice these sentences.

1. Who was **Columbus?**   **A navigator.**
        a navigator?   Columbus
        born in Genoa?   Columbus

2. Columbus **sailed far north to England.**
             far south to the Azores
             across the Atlantic

Quiz
Write <u>true</u> or <u>false</u> after each sentence.

1. Columbus called the people in North America "Indians." _____

2. Columbus found the Indies before he went to North America. _____

3. Columbus went east to find America. _____

4. The Indians lived in one big group. _____

5. Some of the Indians were hunters. _____

6. The Indians took care of the land. _____

7. We call Europeans "native Americans." _____

8. Columbus sailed on ships to find America. _____

Lesson 3
Explorers and Missionaries

Competency Objective
After completing Lesson 3, students will be able to **(1)** name 2 reasons why Europeans came to live in the New World.

After Columbus found America, many other Europeans came to the *New World*. Many people were *explorers*. They wanted to find gold and to *claim* land for their countries.

In the 1500s, the explorers from Spain claimed more land than the explorers from France or England. The Spanish explorers took the land from the Indians. The Spanish claimed the land in North America that is now Mexico and the southern part of the United States. The English and French explorers claimed smaller pieces of land that are now in Canada.

Amerigo Vespucci was an explorer for Spain and Portugal. He made a map of the New World and named the land "America."

The Spanish explorers claimed large portions of land in America. *Later,* they *sent* missionaries to the New World. The missionaries *built* missions and *taught* the Christian religion to the Indians. The missionaries *brought* horses, cows, and other animals with them. They were the first Europeans to live in North America.

People from other countries in Europe heard about America. These countries sent explorers to learn about the new land. These European countries also sent colonists to the New World. The English sent explorers. The Dutch sent explorers. The French sent explorers. John Cabot explored North America for England. Henry Hudson explored North America for the Netherlands and England. Jacques Cartier and Samuel Champlain explored North America for France.

Activity Section

Activity 1 (pair or group work)
Ask a classmate the following questions. Then write the answers.

1. Who gave the name "America" to the New World?

_____

2. Which European countries sent explorers to North America?

_____

3. Which explorers claimed more land in the 1500s?

_____

4. What did the missionaries teach the Indians?

_____

5. Who claimed land that is now part of Canada?

_____

Activity 2
Complete these sentences.

In the 1500s, many _____ came to the New World to find

gold. They took _____ from the Indians. The explorers

from _____ claimed more land than the explorers from

other countries. The first Europeans to live in North America were the

_____. They wanted to teach _____ to the

Indians.

Activity 3
Practice these sentences.

1. The **Spaniards** sent **missionaries** and soldiers.

     French   explorers
     English   *preachers*

2. Who **taught religion?** The Europeans did.

       sent soldiers
       built missions
       claimed land
       brought animals

3. They wanted to **teach religion.**

            claim land
            find gold

4. What did Columbus find? He found **the New World.**

                land
                North America
                Indians

Quiz

Write the letter of the correct answer in the blank.

1. _____ claimed land for their country.

    a. Indians   b. Explorers   c. Missionaries

2. The explorers wanted to find _____.

    a. gold   b. horses   c. Indians

3. Spain took land from the _____.

    a. English   b. Indians   c. Europeans

4. People from _____ brought horses and cows to North America.

    a. Italy   b. India   c. Spain

5. Spain sent people to build _____.

    a. missions   b. houses   c. ships

Lesson 4
English Colonies in the New World

Competency Objectives

After completing Lesson 4, students will be able to **(1)** give reasons why Europeans came to live in the New World and **(2)** identify the number of original colonies.

In the 1600s, many people came to America from England, France, and Spain. They came to America for different *reasons*. Some people came to America because they wanted *political freedom*. Some wanted *religious freedom*. Others wanted to *own* land or to find gold.

Some of the first people to arrive in the northeastern part of the colonies were from England. The English people *founded* the first two permanent colonies on the Atlantic coast: Jamestown and Plymouth.

The colony at Jamestown, Virginia, began in 1607. The London Company in England founded the colony to make money in the New World. Soon the *colonists* learned how to grow *tobacco*. They *grew* tobacco, *sold* the tobacco to people in Europe, and made a lot of money.

A group of people called the Pilgrims began the Plymouth colony. The Pilgrims did not have religious freedom in England, so they left England. They sailed to America on a ship called the Mayflower and arrived at Cape Cod in November 1620.

Life was not *easy* for the Pilgrims the first year in the new country, but the Indians helped them. The Indians taught the Pilgrims how to farm and how to grow corn and other *crops*. The Pilgrims had a celebration of *thanksgiving* with the Indians at the *end* of the first year. This celebration is now called Thanksgiving Day.

Soon the Indians and the Pilgrims *helped* each other, and they traded things they had or made.

Other people from Europe came to the New World. Some of them founded colonies on the eastern shore of America. Each colony made its own laws, and the people in the colony obeyed them. But the government of England *still controlled* most of the colonies. By 1750, there were 13 English colonies in North America.

Activity Section

Activity 1
Practice these sentences.

1. **The Jamestown colonists** came to America in **1607.**

   The Pilgrims   1620
   My friends

2. Some colonists wanted to have **political freedom.**

   religious freedom
   land
   a business

3. People came from **England.**

   France
   Spain
   Mexico

4. **First,** there were **2** colonies.

   Later   more
   Then   13

5. The Indians taught the Pilgrims how to grow **corn.**

   crops
   tobacco
   other things

6. Did people come from **France?** Yes, they did.

   Spain
   England
   Mexico

Activity 2

Match the two columns to complete each sentence.

1. Many people came to America from _____ 13 English colonies.

2. Some people came to America for _____ organized the Plymouth colony.

3. By 1750, there were __1__ England, France, and Spain.

4. Jamestown and Plymouth _____ religious freedom.

5. The Pilgrims came to America _____ on the Mayflower.

6. The Pilgrims _____ in England.

7. There was no religious freedom _____ its own laws.

8. Each colony had _____ helped each other.

9. The Pilgrims and the Indians _____ were the first permanent English colonies.

Quiz

Write true or false after each sentence.

1. All Europeans came to America to own a business. _____

2. The Pilgrims came from England. _____

3. Spanish people founded the first 2 permanent colonies in 1607. _____

4. There were 13 colonies by 1750. _____

5. The Pilgrims taught the Indians to grow crops. _____

Lesson 5
The Colonists Were Unhappy

Competency Objectives

After completing Lesson 5, students will be able to **(1)** identify a reason for the colonists' rebellion and **(2)** name a given incident that caused the colonists to rebel.

The colonists were unhappy with English rule for many reasons. The most important reason was high taxes. England and France fought over the land in the New World. England *obtained most* of the land we know as the United States. But the war cost England a lot of money. The king of England *demanded* that the colonists pay high taxes to pay for the war *debt*.

The colonists enjoyed freedom when they helped the English against the French. But they were not happy with the high taxes, so they sent representatives of the 13 colonies to England. They wanted the representatives to defend their interests. The colonists *believed* that with their representatives present, they would get fair tax laws. The king of England did not accept the representatives from the colonies. When the colonists insisted on representation, the king made them pay higher taxes.

One of the colonists' famous protests against the English high taxes *was called* the Boston Tea Party. People in the colonies drank a lot of tea imported from England. The king placed a high tax on tea. This made the colonists very *angry*.

The colonists decided to take action. They wanted to protest *against* the *unjust* English tax on tea. One night a group of colonists *dressed* as native Americans and *quietly climbed* onto an English ship that was *loaded* with tea. They *threw* the tea over the *side* of the ship. This incident was called the Boston Tea Party. The colonists were *on their way* to rebellion. They wanted to be free from the unjust government of England.

Activity Section

Activity 1

Match the two columns to complete each sentence.

1. England and France   _____ representatives to England.

2. The colonies were on their way   _____ a lot of tea.

3. People in the colonies wanted to send   _____ to rebellion.

4. The king did not accept   _____ native Americans.

5. When the colonists insisted, the king   _____ the colonists' representatives.

6. People in the colonies drank   _____ very angry.

7. The king placed a   _____ high tax on tea.

8. The colonists became   _____ made them pay more taxes.

9. A group of men dressed up as   _____ the Boston Tea Party.

10. This incident was called   __1__ fought a war.

Activity 2

Circle the correct response.

1. The king of England was _____.
   - a. just   b. unjust

2. People in the colonies _____ to pay taxes.
   - a. did not like   b. liked

3. The king _____ change the laws.
   - a. did   b. did not

4. Colonists drank _____ tea.
   - a. a lot of   b. very little

5. The king placed _____ on tea.
   - a. a high tax   b. a low tax

Quiz

Answer the following questions. You can use short or complete answers.

1. Who paid a lot of taxes?

   _____

2. Who made them pay taxes?

   _____

3. The people wanted representation. Did the king accept?

   _____

4. Did the people insist?

   _____

5. Were the colonists happy?

   _____

6. Who dressed up as native Americans?

   _____

7. What did they do?

   _____

8. What do we call this incident?

   _____

Lesson 6
The Colonist and Freedom

Competency Objectives

After completing Lesson 6, students will be able to **(1)** identify July 4 as the birthday of the United States, **(2)** identify the name of the new country, and **(3)** identify who wrote most of the Declaration of Independence.

The colonists *suffered* under English law. They were angry because they *had to pay* high taxes and because the English *punished* them unjustly. Finally, the colonists wrote a Declaration of Rights. This document asked the king to *correct* the problems they complained about. The king did not listen.

The colonists called a meeting in Philadelphia to form a new government. They wanted to write their own laws and to declare their independence from England. They asked Thomas Jefferson to write the Declaration of Independence. On July 4, 1776, the members of the Convention all signed the Declaration of Independence. Americans celebrate July 4 as the birthday of the United States.

Since they declared their independence, the colonists prepared for war with the English army. They formed an army to fight for freedom. The colonists asked George Washington to lead the new American army. Many men and boys from the 13 colonies joined George Washington and became part of Washington's army.

The War of Independence against England is also called the Revolutionary War. The colonists believed in freedom, and they fought *bravely* for it. Many *brave* men *died* during this war. They died for the freedom of all Americans.

After 7 difficult years of *fighting,* Washington's army *won* the war. The free people called themselves Americans. The new country they called the United States of America.

Activity Section

Activity 1
Number the events in correct order.

1. _____ The colonists wanted their own laws.

2. _____ The colonists wanted freedom.

3. _____ Thomas Jefferson wrote the Declaration of Independence.

4. _____ The colonists signed the Declaration of Independence on July 4, 1776.

5. _____ The colonists fought for at least 7 years.

6. _____ They called the new country the United States of America.

7. _____ Many people died during the war.

Activity 2
Choose words from the box. Fill in the blanks to complete each sentence.

Jefferson	birthday
freedom	Washington
Revolutionary War	Declaration

1. The colonists wanted _____.

2. _____ wrote an important document.

3. July 4 is America's _____.

4. _____ led the American army.

5. Colonists fought the _____.

6. The important document was the _____ of Independence.

Quiz

Circle the correct response.

1. America's birthday is _____.
   a. July 6, 1774   b. July 4, 1776

2. _____ wrote the Declaration of Independence.
   a. George Washington   b. Thomas Jefferson

3. The War of Independence is _____.
   a. the Revolutionary War   b. the Indian War

4. The colonists _____.
   a. fought bravely   b. did not fight bravely

5. The colonists fought for _____.
   a. 17 years   b. 7 years

Lesson 7
The First Government

Competency Objectives
After completing Lesson 7, students will be able to **(1)** identify the Articles of Confederation as a plan of government and **(2)** state the purpose of the Constitutional Convention.

When the colonies were *no longer* governed by the king of England, they formed a new government. The new government faced many problems. One of these problems was the different interests of the states. Another problem was that most people did not want *centralized government.* They wanted the states and the people to control government directly. Delegates met in Philadelphia for the Continental Congress and wrote the Articles of Confederation. This document was the basis of a plan of government.

In 1787, the 13 states sent representatives to Philadelphia to a new convention to revise the Articles of Confederation. To make their jobs *easier,* the representatives wrote the Preamble. It begins with the words "We the People of the United States . . ." It *promised* to *protect* the liberty and rights of the people and to establish a Constitution. It was a difficult job. The representatives *disagreed* over equal representation and the balance of *power among* the states. They especially disagreed over the power of the federal government. The representatives worked hard at the convention. When they completed their work and agreed on the new form of government, they wrote the new Constitution.

It was not easy to convince the states to *approve* the new Constitution. At first, the states did not want to give up their power to a central government, but they wanted a unified country; finally they agreed. The people in each state voted in favor of the new Constitution. With the approval of the Constitution by all 13 states, the people of America had a new Constitution and a new form of government.

Activity Section

Activity 1

Circle the correct response.

1. There were representatives of _____ at the new convention.
   a. 12 states   b. 13 states

2. The states _____ over the power of the central government.
   a. agreed   b. disagreed

3. The new convention wrote _____.
   a. the Articles of Confederation b. the new Constitution

4. The new government _____.
   a. faced many problems   b. had no problems

5. All the states _____ the Constitution immediately.
   a. approved   b. did not approve

6. All _____ states approved the Constitution.
   a. 12   b. 13

Activity 2

Write true or false after each sentence.

1. It was easy to approve the new Constitution. _____

2. Colonists wrote the Preamble after they wrote the Constitution. _____

3. The Preamble protected the liberty and rights of the people. _____

4. All 13 states approved the Constitution. _____

5. The states disagreed over equal representation. _____

Activity 3
Practice these sentences.

1. The **convention** approved the **Preamble.**

delegates	Preamble
delegates	Constitution
people	Constitution

2. The **representatives** worked hard.

convention
people

3. Some states wanted **equal representation.**

federal government
total independence
a new form of government

Quiz
Answer the following questions. Use short or complete answers.

1. What are the Articles of Confederation?

_____

2. In what year was the Constitutional Convention?

_____

3. What was the basis of a plan of government?

_____

4. What was the *purpose* of the Constitutional Convention?

_____

5. The new government faced many problems. Name 2.

_____

Lesson 8
The Constitution

Competency Objectives
After completing Lesson 8, students will be able to **(1)** state the year the Constitution was written, **(2)** identify the Constitution as a plan of government, and **(3)** identify the Constitution as the highest law of the land.

The leaders of the 13 states met in Philadelphia, Pennsylvania, in 1787 to write the United States Constitution. Famous men *attended* the Constitutional Convention, among them John Adams, Benjamin Franklin, Thomas Jefferson, and James Madison. James Madison is called the Father of the Constitution, because as the secretary of the Convention, he wrote most of it.

A constitution is a plan of government. The colonists wanted to *ensure* that the government would be by the people, of the people, and for the people. The Constitution was so important that it became the supreme law of the land. The Constitution is above all state constitutions.

The writers of the Constitution divided the document into three parts: the Preamble, the Articles, and the Amendments.

The Preamble begins with the words "We the People of the United States . . ." The Preamble is the introduction to the Constitution. It states that the Constitution is necessary to (a) form a united country, (b) *establish* justice, (c) *insure* peace and order, (d) promote general *welfare,* and (e) secure liberty for ourselves and for others.

The second section of the Constitution is the Articles. These articles indicate the structure of government. It separates the structure of the government into 3 branches: the executive branch, the legislative branch, and the judicial branch. Each branch has special powers and responsibilities. The executive branch *enforces* the laws. The legislative branch makes the laws. The judicial branch explains the laws. Each branch watches over the power and the responsibilities of the other 2 branches. These checks and balances protect us against dictators.

The third section of the Constitution is the Amendments. There are 2 parts to the Amendments. The first 10 amendments are called the Bill of Rights. The rest, numbers 11 to 26, are called amendments. The Bill of Rights guarantees our basic rights. The last amendments were added to protect those rights not covered by the Bill of Rights.

Activity Section

Activity 1 (pair work)

Practice the dialogue with another student.

S-1: What is a constitution?

S-2: It is a plan of government.

S-1: *Tell* me about the United States Constitution.

S-2: It is the highest law of the country.

S-1: Is "the highest law" the same as "the supreme law"?

S-2: Yes, highest and supreme mean the *same* thing.

S-1: That was very interesting. Thanks.

S-2: You're welcome.

Activity 2

Match the two columns to complete each sentence.

1. The United States Constitution is the   ____ is a plan of government.

2. Every state has a   ____ the government must have 3 branches.

3. The United States Constitution is above   ____ state constitution.

4. The United States Constitution says that   ____ control the whole government.

5. One branch of government cannot   __1__ supreme law of the land.

6. A constitution   ____ all state constitutions.

Activity 3

Fill in the blanks.

1. The legislative branch _____ the laws.

2. The executive branch _____ the laws.

3. The judicial branch _____ the laws.

Quiz

Circle the correct response.

1. The supreme law of the United States _____.

   a. is the Constitution   b. are state constitutions

2. The United States Constitution is _____ all
   state constitutions.

   a. below   b. above

3. The Constitution divided the government into _____ branches.

   a. 2   b. 3

4. One branch cannot _____ the whole government.

   a. control   b. divide

5. A constitution is a _____ of government.

   a. place   b. plan

6. The 3 branches of government are _____.

   a. the police, the army, and   b. the legislative, the judicial, and
      the navy   the executive

Lesson 9

The 3 Branches of Government

Competency Objectives
After completing Lesson 9, students will be able to **(1)** name the 3 branches of government and **(2)** identify what each branch of government does.

The government consists of 3 main branches: the executive branch, the legislative branch, and the judicial branch. Each branch is *separate* and has special powers. Each watches over the other.

The legislative branch, or Congress, has 2 parts: the Senate and the House of Representatives. Each state elects members to the House of Representatives in proportion to the number of people living in the state. States with more people have a greater voice in the House of Representatives. The principal function of the legislators is to make laws.

The executive branch consists of the following members: the President, the Vice President, the secretaries of the cabinet, and the heads of federal agencies. The main function of the executive branch is to *enforce* the laws that the legislature makes.

The judicial branch consists of the Supreme Court and various federal courts, such as district courts and circuit courts of appeal. The Supreme Court is the highest court in the country.

The persons who decide cases in the judicial branch are judges. The principal *responsibility* of the judicial branch is to explain the law.

In 1787, the writers of the Constitution wanted all 13 states and all future states to have the same form of government. All states in the Union have the same structure of government: an executive branch, a legislative branch, and a judicial branch.

The separation of powers creates a balance of power. Each branch has its own function and its own responsibility. Each checks and balances the power of the other 2 branches to protect the rights of the people.

Activity Section

Activity 1
Circle the correct response.

1. The government has _____ parts, or branches.
   a. 4   b. 3

2. The legislative branch _____ laws.
   a. makes   b. enforces

3. The executive branch _____ laws.
   a. makes   b. enforces

4. The judicial branch _____ laws.
   a. makes   b. explains

5. The Senate is in the _____ branch.
   a. executive   b. legislative

6. The House of Representatives is in the _____ branch.
   a. executive   b. legislative

7. The President works in the _____ branch.
   a. executive   b. judicial

8. The Supreme Court works in the _____ branch.
   a. executive   b. judicial

9. The Vice President works in the _____ branch.
   a. executive   b. judicial

10. The separation of power creates _____.
    a. checks and balances   b. laws

Activity 2 (pair work)

Practice this interview with another student.

INS Agent: Good afternoon, Mrs. Torres.

Applicant: Good afternoon, Officer Peters.

INS Agent: Are you ready for some questions on government?

Applicant: Yes. I think so.

INS Agent: Okay. Let's see. How many branches are in the government?

Applicant: 3.

INS Agent: Can you name them?

Applicant: Yes. The legislative, the executive, and the judicial.

INS Agent: Where does the President work?

Applicant: He works in the executive branch.

INS Agent: What does the judicial branch do?

Applicant: It explains the laws.

INS Agent: How is the legislative branch divided?

Applicant: The legislative branch has 2 parts: the House of Representatives and the Senate.

INS Agent: Who is the President of the United States of America?

Applicant: He is George Bush.

INS Agent: Very good, Mrs. Torres. Those are all the questions. You knew the answers very well. Congratulations. I will recommend you for permanent residency.

Applicant: Thank you, Officer Peters. The questions were very easy. I was very nervous. I was afraid I would *fail*.

Quiz

Write <u>true</u> or <u>false</u> after each sentence.

1. The executive branch controls the legislative branch and the judicial branch. _____

2. Judges are members of the legislative branch. _____

3. Every state has equal numbers of representatives. _____

4. The Supreme Court is the highest court in the country. _____

5. The President and Vice President elect the legislative branch. _____

Lesson 10
The Executive Branch

Competency Objectives
After completing Lesson 10, students will be able to **(1)** identify qualifications to become President and Vice President, **(2)** state the duration of the terms for President and Vice President, and **(3)** name the branch in which the President and Vice President work.

The executive branch consists of the President, the Vice President, the secretaries of the cabinet, and the heads of independent agencies. The main responsibility of the executive branch is to enforce the laws that Congress writes. It is also the duty of the President to watch over the judicial and legislative branches.

The President is the leader of the nation and the commander in chief of the *armed forces.* The President *runs* the country with the help of the Vice President and the cabinet. They are the President's advisors.

To be President, a person must be a native-born citizen, at least 35 years old, and a resident of the United States for at least 14 years. The Vice President can become President if the President dies or is ill. Therefore, the qualifications for Vice President are the same as for the President.

The Constitution *allows* Presidents to be reelected only once. The term of office is 4 years. At the end of the 4 years, the President can run for reelection. Amendment 22 of the Constitution says that a President cannot run for 3 terms in office. This protects the country from a possible *dictatorship.*

The Vice President presides over the Senate. He votes only in case of a tie. George Bush was Ronald Reagan's Vice President. Citizens elected Bush President in 1988.

The Cabinet members advise the President on certain policy matters. They help the President carry out policies.

The independent agencies provide special services. They also help the President carry out policies.

Activity Section

Activity 1

Choose words from the box. Fill in the blanks to complete each sentence.

native American	4 years
executive branch	enforces
native-born	writes
reelected	

1. Independent agencies are part of the _____.

2. The President is a _____ citizen.

3. The President's term is for _____.

4. The Constitution allows Presidents to be _____.

5. Congress _____ the laws.

6. The President _____ the laws.

Activity 2

Practice these sentences.

1. Who **makes** the laws? **The legislative branch.**

      enforces   The executive branch.
      explains   The judicial branch.

2. Who is the **head of the executive branch?** The President.

      leader of the nation
      chief of the armed forces
      chief executive

3. The President must be a **native citizen.**

      at least 35 years old
      of good moral character
      a leader

Quiz

Circle the correct response.

1. The Vice President of the U.S. is _____ years old.

    a. at least 21   b. at least 35

2. The President is the _____.

    a. leader of Congress   b. leader of the nation

3. The President's term of office is _____.

    a. 4 years   b. 8 years

4. The President _____ be reelected once.

    a. can   b. cannot

5. The _____ is the commander of the armed forces.

    a. Vice President   b. President

6. The President and Vice President work in the _____.

    a. legislative branch   b. executive branch

Lesson 11
The President

Competency Objectives

After completing Lesson 11, students will be able to
(1) identify 2 of the President's responsibilities, **(2)** identify
George Washington as the first President of the U.S., and
(3) identify Abraham Lincoln as the sixteenth President of
the U.S.

The President of the United States is the chief executive of the government. It is the President's duty to enforce the laws of the country with help from the cabinet and the independent federal agencies. The President has a variety of duties to keep the government functioning. It is the President's responsibility to work with the legislative and judicial branches. The President also conducts foreign policy. The President is the head, or the commander in chief, of the armed forces. One of the special duties of the President is to *nominate* judges to the Supreme Court. The President also nominates officials to the cabinet or federal agencies, but these officials must receive approval from Congress.

As part of the check over Congress, the President can refuse to sign, or veto, a bill passed by Congress. The President can also pardon a person found guilty of a federal crime. The President can change the course of history while in office.

There have been 40 Presidents in the U.S. In 1988, citizens elected the 41st President of the country. People remember Presidents for what they did for the country or for what they represented. George Washington was the first President of the U.S. When he died, Henry Lee said, "To the memory of the man, first in war, first in peace, and first in the hearts of his countrymen." Lee and many others considered Washington a respected leader.

Abraham Lincoln was the 16th President of the United States. He *abolished* slavery and ended the Civil War. People remember Lincoln especially for those acts.

People remember Presidents for different reasons. Most remember Theodore Roosevelt for the Rough Riders and the Battle of San Juan Hill in Puerto Rico. Citizens remember Franklin D. Roosevelt because he started the Social Security system. Many remember him also because he led the country out of the Depression. Many people remember John F. Kennedy because he was the first Catholic President and because he inspired a generation of young people.

Activity Section

Activity 1
Match the two columns to complete each sentence.

1. The cabinet and independent agencies   ____ Presidents.

2. Citizens elect   ____ approves or rejects judges.

3. The executive branch   ____ veto a bill passed by Congress.

4. Congress   ____ enforces laws.

5. The President can   ____ help the President.

Activity 2
Circle the correct response.

1. Abraham Lincoln was _____.
   a. the first President   b. the sixteenth President

2. Franklin D. Roosevelt _____.
   a. started the Social Security system   b. fought at San Juan Hill

3. The President has _____.
   a. one duty   b. a variety of duties

4. The Supreme Court is a part of _____.
   a. the President   b. the judicial branch

5. _____ can pardon a federal crime.
   a. The President   b. Congress

6. Someone said that _____ was first in war, first in peace, and first in the hearts of his countrymen.
   a. George Washington   b. Theodore Roosevelt

7. _____ abolished slavery.
   a. Abraham Lincoln   b. George Washington

8. _____ was the first Catholic President.
   a. Abraham Lincoln   b. John F. Kennedy

Quiz

Answer the following questions. Use short or complete answers.

1. Who is the chief executive of the country?

_____

2. Who was George Washington?

_____

3. Who was the sixteenth President of the U.S.?

_____

4. Name 2 things Franklin D. Roosevelt did.

_____

5. Can the President veto a bill?

_____

Lesson 12
The Cabinet and Federal Agencies

Competency Objectives
After completing Lesson 12, students will be able to
(1) identify the role of the cabinet and independent agencies,
(2) name 2 cabinet departments, and **(3)** name at least 2
independent federal agencies.

The President has many responsibilities. To *carry out* these responsibilities, the President appoints many heads of executive departments. There are 2 main departments that help the President: the cabinet and the independent federal agencies.

Today, there are 14 federal departments in the President's cabinet. Each department has a head. The heads of these departments are called secretaries. The only exception is the head of the Department of Justice, who is called the attorney general. The Constitution does not call for a cabinet. However, beginning with George Washington, all the Presidents have appointed people to these positions.

The 14 departments are (1) State, (2) *Treasury,* (3) Defense, (4) Justice, (5) Interior, (6) Agriculture, (7) Commerce, (8) Labor, (9) *Health and Human Services,* (10) Housing and Urban Development, (11) Transportation, (12) Education,

(13) Energy, and (14) Veterans Affairs. Each department has its responsibilities. Some departments are better known than others. For example, the Treasury Department collects taxes; the Justice Department enforces immigration; Health and Human Services administers Social Security and Welfare; Agriculture *gives out* food stamps and food.

There are many different independent federal agencies. Only a few are mentioned here. The U.S. Postal Service *delivers* millions of letters every day. The *Small Business* Administration advises and gives loans to small businesses. The Commission on Civil Rights watches over the civil rights of all citizens.

Activity Section

Activity 1

Circle the correct response.

1. The Treasury Department _____.
   a. collects taxes   b. collects immigrants

2. The Health and Human Services Department _____.
   a. administers Social Security   b. gives out food

3. The Agriculture Department _____.
   a. gives out food   b. enforces immigration

4. The Postal Service is _____.
   a. an independent federal   b. a department
      agency

5. The Small Business Administration gives _____.
   a. business to small people   b. loans to small businesses

6. The Commission on Civil Rights is _____.
   a. part of the Justice   b. an independent federal
      Department   agency

Activity 2

Practice these sentences.

What does the **Small Business Administration** do? **Advises small businesses.**

Postal Service	Deliver mail
Federal Trade Commision	Promotes fair competition
Civil Rights Commission	Watches over civil rights

Activity 3 (pair work)

Ask a classmate the following questions. Then write the answers.

1. How many cabinet departments are there today?

_____

2. What is the head of each department called?

_____

3. Name 2 departments.

_____

4. The attorney general is the head of a department.
   What is the department?

_____

5. Name 2 independent federal agencies.

_____

Quiz

Write true or false after each sentence.

1. Cabinets are independent agencies. _____

2. There are 14 federal departments in the President's cabinet. _____

3. The heads of departments are called secretaries. _____

4. The attorney general is the head of a department. _____

5. The U.S. Postal Service is a federal department. _____

Lesson 13
Legislative Branch

Competency Objectives

After completing Lesson 13, students will be able to **(1)** identify the 2 houses of Congress and name the branch in which they are located and **(2)** state the number of senators elected in each state.

The writers of the Constitution wanted a form of government that would give equal power to small and large states. They wanted to protect the people from dictators. The division of the legislature protects the rights of individual states. The division of power between the branches protects the people from dictators. To keep balance of power between states, the *framers* of the Constitution established 2 different houses in the legislature: the Senate and the House of Representatives.

Each state elects 2 persons to the Senate. These persons are called senators. In the Senate, small states have equal power with larger states. This gives the states an equal opportunity to pass laws that benefit them.

Today the House of Representatives has over 435 members. Each state elects representatives in proportion to the number of people in the state. States are divided into congressional districts. Each district elects a representative. There is a census every 10 years to count the population.

The main function of the legislature, or Congress, is to pass laws and to ensure that both the executive branch and the judicial branch keep *within* their *authority*.

The people of the U.S. give their representatives the power to make laws. The Senate and the House of Representatives work together as the Congress of the United States. The writers of the Constitution wanted two separate groups to approve the laws. They did not want laws passed hurriedly or carelessly. One house checks on the other. The House and the Senate are part of the "System of checks and balances" of power.

Activity Section

Activity 1

Refer to the *passage* to complete this exercise.

The writers of the Constitution _____ a government that

would give _____ to large and small _____.

The division of the _____ protects the rights of individual

_____. The division of power between the branches

_____ the people from _____.

Each state elects _____ persons to the Senate. Each

state elects representatives _____ to the number of people

in the state.

Activity 2

Match the two columns to answer each question.

1. What keeps the balance of power between the states?

2. How many senators does each state elect?

3. What are the 2 houses of Congress called?

4. How many members are there in the House today?

5. What is the main function of Congress?

6. How many senators are there?

_____ 435

_____ the Senate and the
House of Representatives

_____ the division of the legislature

_____ 2

_____ 100

_____ pass laws

Quiz

Circle the correct response.

1. The Senate and the House are part of _____.
   a. the executive branch   b. the legislative branch

2. Each state has _____.
   a. 2 representatives   b. at least 1 representative

3. There is a census _____.
   a. every 4 years   b. every 10 years

4. In the Senate, large states have _____ small states.
   a. equal power to   b. more power than

5. The legislature _____ the executive branch.
   a. watches   b. controls

Lesson 14
The Senate

Competency Objectives
After completing Lesson 14, students will be able to
(1) identify qualifications to become a senator and **(2)** identify functions of a senator.

The Senate is the smaller of the 2 houses of Congress. It has 100 members. The House and the Senate *share* the responsibility of making laws. Each of these houses also has a separate responsibility. The House *introduces* bills about the budget or taxes. The House also *impeaches* officials. The Senate determines the innocence or guilt of the impeached officials. It also confirms or denies *appointments* the President makes. Another function of the Senate is to *ratify treaties* between the U.S. and other governments. Each state elects 2 senators. To be a senator, a person must be at least 30 years old and a native or naturalized citizen. A *candidate* for senator must also live in the state for at least 9 years. A senator must live in the state he or she wants to represent.

As a part of Congress, senators have the responsibility to check and balance the power of the executive and judicial branches. Senators can make laws to collect *taxes* or *print* money. They can make laws on naturalization. Only the Senate along with the House of Representatives can declare *war*.

People elect senators for longer terms than representatives. They are elected for 6-year terms. There is no limit to the number of times senators may be reelected. In some cases, voters keep senators in Congress for a very long time. Often these senators gain *seniority* and become heads of committees that distribute money to different programs. A state can benefit *greatly* if one of its senators is the head of an important committee.

Citizens choose senators at a national election. This election is held in November of each even numbered year. In this way the Senate never has only new Senators. The Senate always has a 2/3 majority of experienced Senators.

Activity Section

Activity 1

Circle the best answer in each case based on the passage.

1. Each state elects _____.
   a. 1 senator   b. many senators   c. 2 senators

2. Senators must _____.
   a. have money   b. be a resident of that state   c. live anywhere in the U.S.

3. Senators may be _____.
   a. permanent residents   b. naturalized citizens   c. 29 years old

4. Senators may _____.
   a. confirm appointments   b. make appointments   c. run the government

5. The main function of the Senate is _____.
   a. to make money   b. to make laws   c. to collect taxes

Activity 2

Practice these sentences.

1. Who **writes laws?** Senators do.
        confirms appointments
        ratifies treaties
        rejects appointments

2. A senator must be **at least 30 years old.**
        a citizen at least 9 years
        a resident of that state

3. The Senate **makes laws.**
        ratifies treaties
        approves appointments
        rejects appointments

Activity 3 (pair work)

Practice the dialogue with another student.

S-1:   I want to be a senator one day.

S-2:   Are you a naturalized citizen?

S-1:   Not yet, but I'll be a resident.

S-2:   Senators must be citizens.

S-1:   Then I'll be a citizen.

S-2:   How old are you?

S-1:   I'm 25 years old.

S-2:   You have to be at least 30 years old.

S-1:   Then I'll wait.

Quiz

Answer the following questions. Use short or complete answers.

1. Are you a permanent resident?

_____

2. How old are you?

_____

3. Where do you live? (state)

_____

4. How long is a senator's term?

_____

5. What is a senator's main function?

_____

Lesson 15
The House of Representatives

Competency Objectives

After completing Lesson 15, students will be able to
(1) identify the qualifications to become a representative and
(2) identify functions of the House of Representatives.

The House of Representatives is the larger of the 2 houses of Congress. Every district in a state elects members to the House of Representatives. In this part of the legislature, states with large populations have more power than states with small populations. This provides some balance of power between the states.

Most states are divided into districts, and each district chooses a representative. Every 10 years, the government has a census to count the number of people per district throughout the country. States can either lose or gain representatives every 10 years.

As part of Congress, the House of Representatives *shares* legislative responsibilities with the Senate. Their main responsibility is to write laws. Another responsibility is to watch and check the power of the executive and judicial branches. Like the senators, representatives can regulate money and trade. This function includes authorization to print money, to borrow money, to place and collect taxes,

and to regulate trade between the states. Representatives and senators also share other responsibilities. They provide money to maintain the army, navy, and air force. They also make laws about naturalization of *aliens;* they *regulate* the system of *weights* and *measures;* they pass laws to govern the District of Columbia. Senators and representatives may also declare war. To be a representative, a person must be a citizen for at least 7 years, at least 25 years old, and a resident of the state he or she represents. Representatives serve for 2 years. This means they have to campaign every 2 years. *Yet* many representatives stay in their positions for many years and gain seniority. It helps a state to have senior representatives since they often become heads of committees that may help their state to get more money. These representatives may also help to pass laws that benefit the people in their states.

Activity Section

Activity 1

Match the two columns to complete each sentence.

1. The House of Representatives is   ____ can declare war.

2. Each district of a state   ____ divided into districts.

3. States with smaller populations   ____ every 10 years.

4. Most states are   ____ elects representatives.

5. There is a census   ____ every 2 years.

6. There is an election for representatives   ____ of people in the country.

7. The Senate and the House of Representatives   ____ have fewer representatives.

8. A census counts the number   ____ is the larger of the 2 houses of Congress.

Activity 2

Write true or false after each sentence.

1. The people elect representatives every 6 years. _____

2. Each district elects representatives. _____

3. The House of Representatives has fewer members than the Senate. _____

4. States with smaller populations have fewer representatives. _____

5. The number of representatives is always the same. _____

Activity 3

Practice these sentences.

1. Representatives and senators **share responsibilities.**

> regulate trade
> provide money
> make laws

2. Every **4** years we elect a **President.**

> 2   representative
> 6   senator
> 4   governor

Quiz

Circle the correct response.

1. A representative must be at least _____.

   a. 30 years old   b. 25 years old

2. A representative must be a citizen for at least _____.

   a. 9 years   b. 7 years

3. Representatives _____.

   a. introduce bills   b. command the armed forces

4. Most states are divided into _____.

   a. provinces   b. districts

5. The House shares legislative responsibilities with _____.

   a. the President   b. the Senate

Lesson 16
From Bills to Laws

Competency Objectives
After completing Lesson 16, students will be able to
(1) explain how a bill becomes a law in simple terms and
(2) give 2 examples of checks or balance of power.

Only Congress can make laws. A law can begin in either the Senate or the House of Representatives. However, only representatives can introduce tax or budget *bills*. A bill begins with the idea for a law. The *procedure* for a bill to become law is not only complicated, but also very political.

If a senator or a representative has an idea for a law, he or she presents the bill to a committee. The committee may do 1 of 4 things. It can *amend,* or change, the bill. If the committee does not like it, it can *rewrite* the bill. If it wants to *kill* the bill, the committee ignores it. But if the committee likes the bill, it sends it to its house of Congress for debate.

When one of the houses gets the bill, it can do a number of things with it. Many times, different representatives or senators amend the bill. Sometimes representatives have debates about the bill for long periods. Finally, they vote to pass or to defeat it. If the first house passes a bill, it goes to the other house.

The other house must go through the *same procedure* as the first house to try to pass a bill. It begins as a bill in a committee.

Then, if amended and passed, it is sent to the full house. There, the other legislators debate over the bill. Sometimes legislators amend a bill. When they do, they may *add* their favorite *items* to it. Finally, the second house must vote on the bill. Both houses must approve bills.

Even if both houses approve a bill, it is not law. The President has to sign the bill before it becomes law. The President may do 1 of 3 things. If the President signs the bill, it becomes law. The President may ignore the bill. Then if Congress *stays* in session, this bill becomes law. If Congress does not stay in session, it does not become law. The President may also *veto* the bill. Then it does not become law. This is the President's check of Congress's power. Congress can approve a bill over the veto of the President. To do this requires 2/3 votes of both houses. This is Congress's check of the President's power.

Activity Section

Activity 1
Write <u>true</u> or <u>false</u> after each sentence.

1. Only the Senate can make laws. _____

2. The procedure for a bill to become law is very political. _____

3. To amend a bill means to make changes. _____

4. The President must sign every bill. _____

5. A bill must pass both houses. _____

Activity 2 (pair or group work)
Ask a classmate the following questions. Then write the answers.

1. Who makes laws?

_____

2. Can a woman be a senator?

_____

3. A committee may do 1 of 4 things about a bill. Name all 4.

_____

4. Who introduces tax or budget bills?

_____

5. The President can check Congress's power. How?

_____

Activity 3
Indicate the order in which bills are approved.

____ The committee can change, rewrite, kill, or send the bill to its house.

____ The bill goes to the other house.

____ The second house sends the bill to the President.

____ Representatives present bills to a committee.

____ The President signs or vetoes the bill.

____ The second house also approves the bill.

Quiz
Circle the correct response.

1. An idea for a law is _____.
   a. a bill   b. an appeal

2. To change a bill is to _____.
   a. amend it   b. ignore it

3. To pass a bill is to _____.
   a. kill it   b. approve it

4. Congress can pass a law over the President's veto with _____ of the votes from both houses.
   a. 2/3   b. 100%

5. _____ checks and balances between the executive and legislative branches.
   a. There are not   b. There are

Lesson 17
The Judicial Branch

Competency Objectives

After completing Lesson 17, students will be able to (1) name the branch in which the Supreme Court works, (2) identify the Supreme Court as the highest court in the land, (3) identify the function of the judicial branch, and (4) identify the right to appeal.

The federal court system is the main part of the judicial branch. The responsibility of the judicial branch is to explain and interpret the laws. The federal courts not only interpret the laws, but also judge the most important cases.

The Supreme Court is a part of the judicial branch. Nine persons serve on this court. The 9 persons who serve on the Supreme Court are called Supreme Court justices. The Supreme Court justices interpret and decide how the Constitution applies to cases. It is the highest court in the land, and its decisions are final.

The Supreme Court checks and balances the power of the legislative and executive branches. It *ensures* that they both keep within the Constitutional *requirements*. Although the President *nominates* Supreme Court justices, Congress must approve their *nominations*. If approved, the justices serve for life.

It would be impossible for the Supreme Court to hear all cases. *Therefore,* there are different levels of courts. There are local, state, and federal courts. These courts give all *accused* a just *hearing*. A case may be heard in one of the district courts, in a circuit court, or finally in the Supreme Court.

Every person has the *right* to a just and *speedy* trial. If a person is accused of a federal crime, he or she is judged in one of the 94 district courts in the country. If the *lawyer* and the accused do not agree with the *verdict,* or decision, they can *appeal* to a higher court called the circuit court. If they still believe that the verdict is unjust and *wrong,* they can appeal to the Supreme Court. When the Supreme Court makes a decision, that decision is final. The Supreme Court is the highest court in the land. No one may appeal its decision.

Activity Section

Activity 1
Choose words from the box. Fill in the blanks to complete each sentence.

local	judicial	justices
other	explains	final

1. There are federal, state, and _____ courts.

2. The federal court system is the main part of the _____ branch.

3. There are 9 _____ on the Supreme Court.

4. The judicial branch _____ the laws.

5. The Supreme Court checks and balances the power of the

   _____ branches.

6. Supreme Court decisions are _____.

Activity 2 (pair work)
Practice the dialogue with another student.

S-1:   Hi Susana, what's the matter?

S-2:   They accused Marcos of a crime.

S-1:   Is he guilty?

S-2:   Of course he isn't!

S-1:   What are you going to do?

S-2:   I will appeal. This is the United States.

S-1:   That's right. Here you are innocent until *proven* guilty.

S-2:   I'll get a good lawyer.

S-1:   Good idea.

Activity 3 (pair or group work)

Ask a classmate the following questions. Then write the answers.

1. Who nominates Supreme Court justices?

_____

2. Who approves the nomination of Supreme Court justices?

_____

3. How long do Supreme Court justices serve?

_____

4. How many Supreme Court justices are there?

_____

5. You do not agree with a court decision. What can you do?

_____

6. Which is the highest court in the land?

_____

Quiz

Write <u>true</u> or <u>false</u> after each sentence.

1. The Supreme Court is a part of the executive branch. _____

2. The Supreme Court is the highest court of the land. _____

3. The judicial branch explains and interprets the laws. _____

4. Supreme Court verdicts are final. _____

5. Congress nominates Supreme Court justices. _____

6. Supreme Court justices serve for life. _____

7. Judges cannot sentence a person without a trial. _____

Lesson 18
The First 4 Presidents

Competency Objectives
After completing Lesson 18, students will be able to
(1) identify George Washington as the first President of the
United States, **(2)** identify Thomas Jefferson as the third
President of the United States, and **(3)** identify Thomas
Jefferson as the person who wrote the Declaration of
Independence.

The United States had some great leaders as first Presidents. George Washington, Thomas Jefferson, and James Madison were Presidents in the early years. They were great leaders. John Adams was also one of our early Presidents. The founders of this nation admired George Washington for his leadership qualities. He led his men on many missions during the French and Indian War. Later, when the colonies *held* the first Continental Congress, he was sent as a delegate to represent Virginia. The delegates recognized Washington's military experience and named him Commander of the Revolutionary Army. He and his men fought hard against the experienced English army and won the war.

Washington's work for his country did not end with the war. He was sent as a delegate to the Constitutional Convention held in Pennsylvania. As a *respected* leader of the group, he helped the delegates reach agreement on the Constitution. He was so highly respected that the people of the

nation elected him the first President of the United States. President Washington decided to retire from politics after his second term. Washington was a great leader because he led his nation not only in war, but also in peace.

John Adams was the second President of the United States. He had experience in government because he was Vice President under George Washington. His term of office was difficult because he followed George Washington as President and because he made difficult and unpopular decisions. He *negotiated* peace with both France and England. *Although* it was an unpopular decision, he is *remembered* for keeping the young country out of war at a time when the government did not have money for an army.

Thomas Jefferson is one of America's favorite heroes. He served his country well on many occasions. He wrote the Declaration of Independence. He served as Secretary of State under George Washington. Later, Jefferson was the first ambassador to

France. When he *returned,* he ran for President but lost. Because he had the second highest number of votes, he became Vice President. He was later elected third President of the United States. As President, he doubled the size of the country with the Louisiana Purchase from France. Jefferson's many *accomplishments earned* him a place in history.

James Madison played an important role in the development of the United States. He was the secretary of the Constitutional Convention and helped to write the Constitution. After Jefferson completed his term in office, the people elected Madison the fourth President. His term in office was very difficult. He wanted peace, but Congress wanted war with *Britain* and Spain. The British were supporting Indian *attacks* on the Americans in the West. As problems *continued,* and because the Americans wanted more *territory,* Madison *declared* war against Britain in 1812.

Activity Section

Activity 1
Circle the correct response.

1. _____ was the first President of the United States.

    a. Thomas Jefferson   b. George Washington

2. _____ was the third President of the United States.

    a. Thomas Jefferson   b. James Madison

3. Washington was the _____.

    a. commander of the army   b. first ambassador to France

4. Washington served _____.

    a. 1 term   b. 2 terms

5. John Adams was a(n) _____ President.

    a. popular   b. unpopular

6. John Adams made _____ decisions.

    a. easy   b. difficult

7. John Adams negotiated peace with _____ .

    a. France and Spain   b. France and England

Activity 2

Write true or false after each sentence.

1. George Washington was a great leader. _____

2. Thomas Jefferson was the second President of the U.S. _____

3. Washington attended the first Continental Congress. _____

4. Jefferson was the third President of the U.S. _____

5. Madison was the secretary of the Continental Congress. _____

6. Madison was the second President of the U.S. _____

7. Madison declared war against Britain in 1812. _____

8. Jefferson wrote the Declaration of Independence. _____

Activity 3

Practice these sentences.

1. Washington **negotiated** for his country.
> fought
> worked

2. Washington was a **leader.**
> commander
> fighter
> President

3. Jefferson served as **Secretary of State.**
> ambassador to France
> Vice President
> President

4. Who was **the first President of the U.S.? George Washington**.

George Washington?	The first President
the third President of the U.S.	Thomas Jefferson
Thomas Jefferson	The third President

Quiz

Match the two columns to complete each sentence.

1. Jefferson   _____ kept the young country out of war.

2. The nation elected Washington   _____ fought against the English and won.

3. The nation elected Jefferson   _____ declared war against Britain in 1812.

4. Washington   _____ with the Louisiana Purchase.

5. Madison   _____ the third President of the U.S.

6. The size of the U.S. doubled   _____ wrote the Declaration of Independence.

7. Adams   _____ the first President of the U.S.

8. The Constitutional Convention was held   _____ in Pennsylvania.

Lesson 19
The Civil War

Competency Objectives

After completing Lesson 19, students will be able to **(1)** identify the 16th President of the United States, **(2)** state the importance of the 16th President, and **(3)** identify causes of the Civil War.

The Civil War, or the War between the States, was one of the most difficult times for the United States. The war divided the country into two *enemy camps:* the Union Army, in the North, and the Confederate Army, in the South. Civil wars are destructive. They *match* brothers against brothers and friends against friends.

Many *issues* led to the Civil War. One of the principal causes of the war was the issue of *slavery.* Slavery in the South kept the economy of the South strong. The southern politicians and businessmen knew that if they abolished slavery, the economy of the South would fall. Another reason for the war was the right of a state to separate from the union of the United States. Another problem was the election of Abraham Lincoln as the 16th President of the United States.

Four days after Lincoln was elected, the southern states *left* the Union and *formed* the Confederate States of America. The southern soldiers, or the rebels, wore a gray-brown uniform and *marched* behind the Dixie flag. The South, led by General Robert E. Lee, fought hard to keep their

way of life. They felt that the central or federal government wanted too much control over their *lives.* Many young men lost their lives during the Civil War. It destroyed the economy of the South.

The northern army was the Union Army. The soldiers, or Yankees, wore blue uniforms. Although the Yankees had more money and more soldiers, it took a long and *bloody* battle that lasted 5 years to defeat the South. Finally, after the death of hundreds of thousands of boys and young men on each side, the Civil War ended. The war *destroyed* the southern countryside and burned many southern cities.

Lincoln *hated* the war, but he wanted the states to be a Union under one government. He also wanted all states to obey the laws of the Constitution. He made many famous *speeches* about the Union and about liberty. After the bloody 3-day battle at Gettysburg, Lincoln gave his Gettysburg *Address.* In this speech, he *emphasized* that the United States was indivisible. After the surrender of the South, the country began rebuilding the cities and the economy destroyed by the war. Lincoln continued his work for freedom. He issued the Emancipation Proclamation, which set all slaves free. Once the war was *over* and the Union preserved, Lincoln was ready to *rebuild* and *strengthen* the country. However, only a few days after the war was over, the 16th President of the United States was *assassinated*.

Activity Section

Activity 1

Refer to the passage to complete this exercise.

The Civil War was a _____ time for the United States.

The War divided the country into two _____ camps: the

Union Army, in the North, and the _____, in the South.

Civil wars are destructive because they match _____

against _____ and friends _____ friends.

One of the principal causes of the war was _____. Slavery

kept the _____ of the South strong. Another reason for

the war was the _____ of a state to separate from the

_____. Another problem was the election of

_____ as the 16th President of the U.S.

Activity 2 (pair or group work)
Match the two columns to answer each question.

1. The southern states left the Union. When?   _____ southern soldiers

2. Who were the rebels?   _____ when Lincoln was elected

3. What was the name for the northern soldiers?   _____ a few days after the war

4. Who wore blue uniforms?   _____ 5 years

5. What did Lincoln want the states to obey?   _____ hundreds of thousands

6. When was Lincoln assassinated?   _____ Yankees

7. The Civil War lasted a few years. How many?   _____ War between the States

8. How many people were killed in the Civil War?   _____ the Constitution

9. What is the Civil War also called?   _____ Lincoln

10. Who issued the Emancipation Proclamation?   _____ northern soldiers

Quiz
Circle the correct response.

1. Lincoln was the _____ of the U.S.
   a. third President   b. 16th President

2. Lincoln _____.
   a. wrote the Constitution   b. abolished slavery

3. One of the causes of the Civil War was _____.
   a. economic differences   b. brothers against brothers

4. The Civil War was also about _____.
   a. control of the   b. control of state government
      central government

5. Lincoln wanted a _____ country.
   a. united   b. divided

Lesson 20
The Industrial Age

Competency Objectives

After completing Lesson 20, students will be able to **(1)** name one invention **(2)** identify the industrial age.

The 20th *century* created great changes in America. The first change was geographic. America *spread* across to the west. It included not only the Louisiana Purchase, but also the Northern *Passage,* all the way to Oregon. The U.S. got the northern part of Mexico, which included California, Texas, Colorado, Arizona, and New Mexico, after the war with Mexico. The second change was population *movement.* Young people left small towns and farms and went to the city to look for *jobs* and new opportunities. The third change was economic. Factories created new jobs. For more than 100 years America was an agricultural society. Then, the new industrial *age* began. America changed forever.

The Yankee spirit of adventure and freedom and the belief that everyone could *get rich* led to new and *exciting* inventions. *Moreover,* the use of *coal* and *rivers* for electricity provided the power to use large machines. Inventors such as Eli Whitney, Henry Ford, and Thomas Edison changed work in America greatly. Factories *ruled* the economy using new inventions. Eli Whitney's *cotton gin* made *cloth* faster than 20 workers could. Thomas Edison invented the *light bulb,* and *factories* stayed open

longer hours. Henry Ford improved the factory system when he introduced the assembly line. Everyone did one job *over and over.* In that way, they produced cars faster. *Furthermore,* they discovered that production could go faster if products looked the same. *Mass* production *entered* the industrial world. The way people worked changed forever. A great number of small shops closed. The competition from big industry was too much. There was little *room* in these new industries for artists or *craftsmen.* The *worker* was a slave to a machine that never got *tired,* never got *hungry,* and never *complained.*

Industrialization changed American society. Men and women left the farms to seek jobs in the factories. There were so many workers seeking jobs that owners paid low *wages.* There were no laws to protect workers. Since the machines could work all day, the owners wanted the workers to work long hours. Many women and children went to work for very low wages and worked in *unhealthy* conditions. Sometimes they stood long hours *without breaks* or *inhaled lint* that was dangerous to their *health.* Men, women, and children became part of a great machine, the factory.

Activity Section

Activity 1
Practice these sentences.

1. The **first** change was **geographic.**

   second   population movement
   third   economic
   fourth   industrial

2. **George Washington Carver** was an inventor.

   Eli Whitney
   Alexander Graham Bell
   Thomas Edison

3. **Alexander Graham Bell** invented the **typewriter.**

   Thomas Edison   light bulb
   Eli Whitney   cotton gin
   Elias Howe   sewing machine

4. Many **people** left the farms and went to the factories.

   women
   men
   children
   boys
   girls

5. **Men** left the farms to seek jobs.

   Women
   Young people
   Farmers

Activity 2

Write <u>true</u> or <u>false</u> after each sentence.

1. The agricultural age began in the 20th century. _____

2. During the industrial revolution many people worked in unhealthy conditions. _____

3. Electricity helped machines work faster. _____

4. For more than 100 years, America was a farming society. _____

5. Americans invented machines to help the poor. _____

6. Only men worked in factories. _____

7. All workers earned a lot of money. _____

8. Industrialization did not change American society. _____

Quiz

Match the two columns to complete each sentence.

1. Eli Whitney   _____ produced cars.

2. Henry Ford   _____ invented the light bulb.

3. Thomas Edison   _____ pay per hour, week, or day.

4. Wage is   _____ great changes in America.

5. The 20th century created   _____ look the same.

6. Mass-produced articles   _1_ invented the cotton gin.

Lesson 21

World War I and World War II

Competency Objectives

After completing Lesson 21, students will be able to
(1) identify 2 countries that fought with the United States in World War I, **(2)** identify 2 countries that fought with the United States in World War II, **(3)** identify what happened at Pearl Harbor, and **(4)** identify how Hiroshima was destroyed.

In 1914, Europe was at war. Germany and Austria fought against England, France, and Russia. America, under President Wilson, wanted to stay neutral. But soon German submarines *sank* American *ships,* and many people died at sea. Finally, in 1917, after the Germans sank the Lusitania and 1,000 people died, Congress declared war on Germany. America entered World War I.

America began to change its economy to a war economy. The draft, the selection of young men by lottery, began. Young men were sent, as the *song* says, "Over there . . ." to help Europe win the war. The young new soldiers, the Yanks, took new planes, money, and war supplies to the armies in Europe. With American help, the English and French finally won the war. Germany *signed* the armistice in 1918. America's role in the world changed forever.

In 1939, Germany attacked Europe again. Two armies were at war. France, England, and Russia were the Allied powers. Germany, Italy, and Japan were the Axis powers. America was neutral. America did not want to send people to war again.

On December 7, 1941, Japan *bombed* Pearl Harbor and destroyed the American *fleet.* Congress declared war on Germany, Italy, and Japan and *joined* the Allied Forces. Soldiers fought the war on 2 fronts: the western front in Europe and the war in the Pacific. Americans entered the war with determination and economic power. It was a terrible war. Hundreds of thousands of men, women, and children died during this war on all sides of the world. This was really a world war — one that no one would ever *forget*. The Allied forces defeated the Axis powers in 1945. General Eisenhower was commander of those forces in Europe. General Douglas MacArthur led the forces in the Pacific against the

Japanese army and navy. After a long war, the Japanese refused to *surrender*.

Early in the morning on August 6, 1945, an American bomber *dropped* the first atomic bomb on Hiroshima, Japan. This first bomb alone killed at least 70,000 people. Still the Japanese did not surrender.

On August 9, American forces dropped a second bomb on Nagasaki. This new atomic bomb changed the face of the war. These 2 bombs left *traces* of radiation in the bodies of the *survivors* and in the earth they walked on. Japan surrendered. World War II ended.

Activity Section

Activity 1 (pair or group work)

Ask a classmate the following questions. Then write the answers.

1. Who were allies with the U.S. in World War I?

_____

2. When did America enter the war?

_____

3. What did the German submarines do?

_____

4. When did Germany sign the armistice?

_____

5. What countries fought against the U.S. in World War I?

_____

Activity 2

Circle the correct response.

1. The U.S. entered World War I in _____ .
   a. 1917   b. 1914

2. _____ declared war on Germany.
   a. Congress   b. The President

3. Germany signed the armistice in _____.
   a. 1918   b. 1917

4. World War II began in _____.
   a. 1939   b. 1951

5. The _____ bombed Pearl Harbor.
   a. Japanese   b. Germans

Activity 3

Circle the correct response.

1. Who fought against England, France, and Russia in 1914?
   a. Germany and Austria   b. Italy and Germany   c. Italy and Austria

2. When did America declare war on Germany?
   a. in 1914   b. in 1918   c. in 1917

3. When did World War II begin?
   a. in 1939   b. in 1941   c. in 1945

4. When did the Japanese bomb Pearl Harbor?
   a. in December 1941   b. in December 1914   c. in December 1939

5. Where did the Americans drop the first atomic bomb?
   a. Hiroshima   b. Nagasaki   c. Tokyo

Quiz

Write <u>true</u> or <u>false</u> after each sentence.

1. England, France, and Russia fought on the same side in World War I. _____

2. America did not enter World War II. _____

3. France, England, Russia, and the U.S. were allies in World War II. _____

4. The Japanese bombed Pearl Harbor. _____

5. The Americans bombed Japan. _____

Lesson 22
The Depression

Competency Objectives

After completing Lesson 22, students will be able to
(1) identify the President during the Depression and
(2) identify one cause of the Depression.

Americans suffered greatly during the Depression of 1929. There were many reasons for the Depression. Factories produced too many products. *Tariffs* were high on *imports,* so trade between countries was difficult. New machines put people out of work. One of the big reasons for the Depression was the *Stock Market Crash.* This crash happened on Tuesday, October 29, 1929.

The Stock Market Crash *caused* many problems. Banks *closed,* and people lost their money. Factories closed, and millions of people lost their jobs. They did not have money to buy goods, so stores closed. Many people lost their homes. Many *businessmen committed* suicide. Some people died because they had no food. Others died because they had no medical attention. There were long lines of people waiting for food. These lines were called the "bread lines." Americans suffered for 10 long years.

In 1932, Franklin D. Roosevelt became President. He promised to improve the life of every American. The President and Congress promised jobs for people out of work. Congress started the WPA, the Works Progress Administration, and the PWA, the Public Works Administration. These projects *built roads,* schools, *libraries,* public offices, *bridges,* and other buildings. The government *lent* money for home *mortgages* and *insured* banks and people's savings. President Roosevelt also started the Social Security system to help people during *retirement.* Roosevelt's big plan, the New Deal, placed America on track again.

Activity Section

Activity 1
Write true or false after each sentence.

1. There was only one reason for the Depression. _____

2. The Stock Market Crash was the big reason for the Depression. _____

3. Banks closed during the Depression. _____

4. Some people died because they had no medical attention. _____

5. During the Depression everyone had food. _____

Activity 2 (pair or group work)
Read each sentence. Write a negative sentence to say what is not correct.

1. The Depression was in 1829.

   The Depression was not in 1829.

2. Factories were open.

   _____

3. Banks were open.

   _____

4. Trade between countries was easy.

   _____

5. The President promised money for everyone.

   _____

6. Low tariffs caused economic problems.

   _____

Activity 3

Practice these sentences.

1. **Banks** closed. People lost their **savings.**

Factories	jobs
Businesses	homes
Stores	food

2. Many people lost their **jobs.**

homes
businesses
friends

3. The government **started Social Security.**

helped people
started the Public Works Administration
insured banks

Quiz

Answer the following questions. Use short or complete answers.

1. When did the stock market crash?

_____

2. Who was the President during the Depression?

_____

3. What were the "bread lines"?

_____

4. What was the New Deal?

_____

5. What does PWA mean?

_____

Lesson 23
Labor Unions

Competency Objectives

After completing Lesson 23, students will be able to **(1)** identify labor unions and **(2)** state 1 reason why workers formed unions.

Workers *started* labor unions for many different reasons. There were many conflicts between labor and business. Industries brought millions of people to the cities to work in factories. Workers worked with machines that were never tired. These machines never complained *either*. Millions of immigrants came from Europe to find a new life. They worked for lower wages. There was a new class of workers. These workers worked by the hour or by the *piece*. These workers never *kept* any of the *profit*.

Workers faced many problems. A *serious* problem was that production *lines moved* too fast. It *seemed* that *owners* did not *care* about the working conditions of workers. These owners *apparently* cared only about *making money*. Many factory buildings were *unsafe*. Conditions were often unhealthy, and many people died from disease. Others died from inadequate working conditions. Wages were low, and workers had to work long hours. There were no job *guarantees* for workers. When they complained, they *lost* their jobs. There was always *someone ready* to work for *less* money.

Workers wanted rights. They formed labor unions. The first labor union, the Knights of Labor, began in 1869. The union demanded an 8-hour day and *better* working conditions. The union also demanded an end to child labor. The union *organized* some of the first *strikes* against employers. At first the union did not *succeed* because workers were *afraid* to *lose* their jobs. In 1881, Samuel Gompers started the AFL, the American Federation of Labor. It had more *success* than the Knights. The AFL *improved* conditions and wages for *skilled* workers. Later, in 1938, workers organized the Congress of Industrial Organizations, the CIO. The CIO called strikes against factories and *businesses* that had poor working conditions, longer than 8-hour days, or low wages.

The *process* of unionizing was not easy. It was difficult and *dangerous*. Many people were *hurt,* and some people died during the strikes. Employers *fired* workers that went on strike from their jobs. Workers now had a way to get some of the benefits of their labor.

Labor unions brought many benefits to

the *working place,* but they also *created* many new problems. Sometimes union leaders used the union money for other *purposes.* Other times union workers paid unjust dues in order to work. Some unions didn't give jobs to workers that were not members. Although there were problems with the system, labor unions helped American workers. They also created a better and *safer* workplace.

Activity Section

Activity 1
Read each sentence. Write an affirmative sentence to say what is correct.

1. Workers didn't start labor unions.

   Workers started labor unions.

2. There weren't conflicts between labor and business.

   _____

3. Workers weren't afraid of losing their jobs.

   _____

4. Immigrants did not come from Europe.

   _____

5. Immigrants did not work for lower wages.

   _____

6. Workers didn't face many problems.

   _____

7. Workers didn't work by the hour or by the piece.

   _____

8. Owners didn't care only about making money.

   _____

Activity 2
Circle the correct response.

1. The _____ organized some of the first strikes.

   a. owners   b. unions

2. At first workers _____ afraid of losing their jobs.

   a. were   b. were not

3. A problem was that production lines moved _____.

   a. fast   b. slowly

4. Conditions were _____, and people died from disease.

   a. healthy   b. unhealthy

5. The first labor union was the _____.

   a. American Federation   b. Knights of Labor
      of Labor

Quiz
Write <u>true</u> or <u>false</u> after each sentence.

1. The AFL is a union. _____

2. Unions protect workers' rights. _____

3. Machines are never tired. _____

4. There are never conflicts between labor and business. _____

5. Some workers worked by the hour or by the piece. _____

Lesson 24
Civil Rights Movements

Competency Objectives
After completing Lesson 24, students will be able to **(1)** name 2 movements that worked for equality for minorities and **(2)** identify Martin Luther King, Jr., as a great civil rights leader.

The civil rights movement began because there was *discrimination* against blacks, Mexicans, native Americans, and Asians. There was discrimination in schools, in jobs, and in housing. There was discrimination even in places where people ate or shopped. The *struggle* for civil rights was long, difficult, and dangerous. Although the Preamble states that the Constitution gives liberty and justice for all, the people in government did not always follow the Constitution. The government in many states was *brutal* against civil rights leaders and *followers.*

After World War II, Roosevelt set up the Fair Employment Practices Committee to protect people of color against discrimination. President Truman started the Committee on Civil Rights. Finally, the Supreme Court decided in 1954, in the case of Brown versus the Board of Education, that it was illegal for schools to segregate children by race. Everyone was not *happy.* Some people *reacted violently* to *positive* civil rights decisions. Martin Luther King, Jr., a great civil rights leader, led peaceful demonstrations for civil rights. Blacks and whites, rich and poor followed King. He had a dream for America. King's vision and civil rights actions *forced* the country to *re-examine* its laws and the Constitution. Martin Luther King, Jr., led his people on a non-violent struggle for their rights. King was assassinated on April 4, 1968, but his dream is still *alive.*

After the Mexican-American War, the states of California, Texas, New Mexico, Colorado, and Nevada became part of the United States. Mexico and the United States signed the Treaty of Guadalupe Hidalgo. This *treaty* said that all Mexican citizens in these areas had equal rights with Americans. The treaty also *protected* their land and property. Furthermore, it protected the Spanish and Mexican culture of the people.

Many early settlers wanted the Mexicans' land. They placed high taxes on property. Many Mexicans lost their land. Other Mexicans left their homes and lands for *fear* of their life. In California, they didn't accept Mexicans as citizens. They did not have all the rights of citizens. Mexicans did not have the right to own land.

In the 1970s, Mexican Americans demanded their rights. In Crystal City, Texas, Dr. Jose Angel Gutierrez led the first student *walk-out*. He registered Mexican Americans to vote under the Raza Unida Party. He won Salva County in an election. Many other leaders led the struggle for civil rights for Mexican Americans. The most famous leaders are Tijerina, in Colorado; Corky Gonzales, in New Mexico; and Cesar Chavez, in California. A group of people made a plan for the Chicano movement. This movement fought for the rights of all Mexican Americans.

The civil rights movements helped minorities. Although there is still discrimination and racism, the chances to *fight back* are better. The U.S. Constitution says that all people have the right to liberty, justice, and an opportunity for *happiness*.

Activity Section

Activity 1
Circle the correct response.

1. The civil rights movement began because there was discrimination _____.
   a. against minorities   b. against Europeans

2. The struggle for civil rights was _____.
   a. easy   b. difficult

3. The case of Brown versus the Board of Education _____ important.
   a. was not   b. was

4. It is _____ for schools to segregate children by race.
   a. illegal   b. legal

5. Martin Luther King, Jr., was a great _____.
   a. President   b. leader

6. King led _____ demonstrations.
   a. violent   b. peaceful

Activity 2

Write the number of the correct answer in the blank.

1. Who was Martin Luther King, Jr.?

2. What did King have for America?

3. When did Texas and California become part of the U.S.?

4. What was the Raza Unida?

5. Who are Tijerina, Gonzales, and Cesar Chavez?

6. What did Truman do for civil rights?

_____ after the Mexican-American War

_____ Mexican American leaders

_____ a dream

_____ He started the Committee on Civil Rights.

_____ a political party

__1__ a great civil rights leader

Quiz

Write true or false after each sentence.

1. There is discrimination in the U.S. today. _____

2. Some state governments were brutal to civil rights leaders. _____

3. The Brown versus the Board of Education case was in 1764. _____

4. Martin Luther King, Jr., was assassinated in 1968. _____

5. The Chicano movement fought for civil rights. _____

6. There is no racism today. _____

7. Discrimination in jobs is legal. _____

8. Cesar Chavez fights for civil rights. _____

Lesson 25
Holidays

Competency Objectives

After completing Lesson 25, students will be able to **(1)** name 3 national holidays, **(2)** identify Presidents' Day, and **(3)** identify the 4th of July as Independence Day.

America celebrates many *holidays.* Some are federal holidays. Others are not. On many of these days, government offices may close. Offices like the INS, the Post Office, City Hall, and county offices may close. On some holidays, many *stores* and places of business may close also. *Besides* a day off from work or school, holidays remind us of important *events* in *our* history.

Independence Day

On every July 4th, Americans celebrate the day in 1776 when they became independent from England. There are usually many *parades* and *fireworks* to celebrate this day.

Columbus Day

Christopher Columbus discovered America. Most of the countries in the Americas celebrate the discovery of America on October 12th. Many cities, especially where there are Italians, have a Columbus Day parade.

Memorial Day

Every year on May 30th, Americans *honor* the men who fought and died to keep Americans free. There are parades and special *services* in *cemeteries* to honor our heroes.

Thanksgiving Day

On the last Thursday of November, families get together to celebrate this day. Many families have a *meal* with *turkey* on Thanksgiving Day. America remembers that the Pilgrims and the native Americans celebrated the first Thanksgiving together. The Pilgrims *thanked* the native Americans. They helped the Pilgrims survive the first winter.

Lincoln's Birthday

Americans remember Abraham Lincoln, the 16th President of the United States, on February 12th. Lincoln *freed* the slaves and *saved* the union.

Washington's Birthday

On February 22nd Americans remember George Washington. He led many important battles during the Revolutionary War and was the first President of the United States. Presidents'

Day celebrates both Lincoln's and Washington's birthdays.

Labor Day

On the first Monday of September, workers have a day off from work. Many families *go on picnics* on Labor Day. They eat *hot dogs, hamburgers,* and *potato salad.* Some people play baseball or other games. For school children, Labor Day is usually the last day of summer vacation before school starts again.

Activity Section

Activity 1 (pair or group work)

Match the two columns to complete each sentence.

1. July 4th is   _____ many families eat turkey.

2. On Thanksgiving Day   _____ Columbus Day.

3. October 12th celebrates   _____ Lincoln and Washington.

4. Presidents' Day celebrates   _____ people who fought and died for America.

5. Memorial Day remembers the   __1__ Independence Day.

Activity 2

Answer the following questions. Use short or complete answers.

1. Who discovered America?

_____

2. When does the U.S. celebrate Columbus Day?

_____

3. When is Thanksgiving Day?

_____

4. When is Labor Day?

_____

5. When do federal offices close?

_____

Activity 3 (pair work)

Read each sentence. Write an affirmative sentence to say what is correct.

1. America doesn't celebrate many holidays.

   America celebrates many holidays.

2. Government offices don't close on federal holidays.

   _____

3. Federal *employees* don't get a day off on federal holidays.

   _____

4. Holidays don't remind us of events in our history.

   _____

5. The 4th of July isn't Independence Day.

   _____

6. Thanksgiving Day isn't the last Thursday in November.

   _____

Quiz

Write true or false after each sentence.

1. The U.S. became independent on July 4, 1776. _____

2. Labor Day, Memorial Day, and Sundays are 3 national holidays. _____

3. The last Thursday in November is Memorial Day. _____

4. Christopher Columbus discovered Italy. _____

5. The INS, the Post Office, and City Halls are businesses. _____

Lesson 26
The American Flag

Competency Objectives
After completing Lesson 26, students will be able to
(1) identify and describe the United States flag, **(2)** state the number of stars and stripes, and **(3)** identify the "Star-Spangled Banner."

Every country in the world chooses a flag. The flag is a symbol of the country. Usually citizens of a country are proud of their flag. Most flags represent certain values of the country. The U.S. flag has *stars* and *stripes.* The U.S. flag has 3 colors. The 3 *colors* are red, white, and blue. The red *represents courage;* the white represents *truth;* and the blue represents *justice.* The flag has 13 stripes. There are 7 red stripes and 6 white stripes. The 13 stripes represent the 13 original colonies of the United States. The flag also has a blue *square* with white stars. Each star represents a state of the Union. There are now 50 stars in the blue square. Each state also has its own flag. Each state chooses symbols and colors that represent the state.

Every country also has a national *anthem.* An anthem is a hymn of *allegiance.* The national anthem of the U.S. is the "Star-Spangled Banner." People *sing* the "Star-Spangled Banner" at official functions. People also sing or *play* the anthem at certain sports events. Francis Scott Key wrote the "Star-Spangled Banner." It begins with the words "Oh say can you see, by the *dawn's* early *light."*

U.S. flag today

U.S. flag in 1776

Activity Section

Activity 1

Complete each sentence with the correct information.

1. The colors of the U.S. flag are _____.

2. The U.S. flag has _____ stripes.

3. The U.S. flag has 50 _____.

4. There are _____ red stripes on the U.S. flag.

5. Each white star represents _____.

6. The first line of the national anthem says _____

_____.

7. The stripes on the U.S. flag represent the original _____.

Activity 2

Circle the correct answer to each question.

1. Do the states have flags?
   a. Yes, they do.   b. No, they don't.

2. How many colors does the U.S. flag have?
   a. 3   b. 5

3. What is the color of the square on the flag?
   a. white   b. blue

4. What is the name of the U.S. national anthem?
   a. "America the Beautiful"   b. "Star-Spangled Banner"

5. What is an anthem?
   a. a hymn   b. a poem

6. What are the first few words of the "Star-Spangled Banner?"
   a. "Oh beautiful . . ."   b. "Oh say can you see . . ."

Activity 3
Practice these sentences.

1. Every country has **a flag.**

     a national anthem
     symbols
     values

2. People play the "Star-Spangled Banner" at **official functions.**

        special events
        sport events
        the Olympics

3. The flag has **3 colors.**

     13 stripes
     50 stars
     a blue square

4. The **flag** represents **the U.S.**

red   courage
white   truth
blue   justice

Quiz
Match the two columns to complete each sentence.

1. The flag is a symbol   ____ 13 stripes.

2. The U.S. flag has   ____ the "Star-Spangled Banner."

3. The national anthem is   ____ hymn of allegiance.

4. An anthem is a   ____ 50 stars on the U.S. flag.

5. There are   ____ of the country.

Lesson 27
The Statue of Liberty

Competency Objectives

After completing Lesson 27, students will be able to **(1)** identify the Statue of Liberty and **(2)** identify what it stands for.

The Statue of Liberty was a *gift* from the people of France. It welcomes people from *all over* the world. France gave the Statue of Liberty to the United States in 1886. To many people, the Statue of Liberty is also a symbol of international *friendship*. Some immigrants *anxiously* await their arrival to New York *harbor*. They know Lady Liberty will *greet* them there.

The Statue of Liberty stands with her arm stretched *upward*. She holds a *torch* to greet immigrants night and day as they enter the United States. The statue is on Liberty Island in the New York harbor. The immigration processing offices on Ellis Island are *across* from the statue. Thousands of immigrants came through the doors of the offices of Ellis Island. To many of these immigrants, Lady Liberty, the statue, is a symbol of a better *future*. To some, it is a symbol of freedom. To others, it is a symbol of opportunity. Today there is a museum on Ellis Island. This museum shows *exhibits* of the different people that came to America. After 100 years, the *sea,*

sun, and *wind* damaged the statue. For her 100th anniversary, Americans from all over the country *donated* money to make her beautiful again. When the workers completed the job, Americans had a special 100-year birthday party for Lady Liberty.

Lady Liberty's 100 year celebration was special. Many thousands of tourists visited Ellis Island to see the Statue of Liberty. Many people decorated their boats and ships with lights and the colors of the American flag. A large number of these boats had a parade around New York Harbor for the occasion. Americans are very proud that Lady Liberty is beautiful again.

Activity Section

Activity 1 (pair or group work)

Read each sentence. Write an affirmative sentence to say what is correct.

1. The Statue of Liberty wasn't a gift from France.

The Statue of Liberty was a gift from France.

2. France didn't give the Statue of Liberty in 1886.

_____

3. The statue isn't a symbol of a better future to many people.

_____

4. There isn't a museum on Ellis Island.

_____

5. The Statue of Liberty doesn't hold a torch.

_____

Activity 2

Circle the correct response.

1. Liberty Island is in _____.
   a. New York   b. the Caribbean

2. The Statue of Liberty welcomes _____.
   a. Americans   b. all people

3. The Statue of Liberty greets immigrants _____.
   a. by night   b. by day and night

4. Lady Liberty was 100 years old _____.
   a. in 1987   b. in 1986

5. Many immigrants enter the country through_____.
   a. Manhattan Island   b. Ellis Island

Quiz

Answer the following questions. Use short or complete answers.

1. What country gave the Statue to the U.S.?

_____

2. What is another name for the Statue of Liberty?

_____

3. What does the Statue of Liberty stand for?

_____

4. Where is Ellis Island?

_____

5. What does Lady Liberty have in her hand?

_____

Lesson 28

The Pledge of Allegiance

Competency Objectives

After completing Lesson 28, students will be able to **(1)** say the Pledge of Allegiance, **(2)** identify the Pledge of Allegiance as a promise, and **(3)** identify the U.S. as a republic.

I pledge allegiance to the flag of the United States of America and to the republic for which it stands, one nation under God, indivisible, with liberty and justice for all.

People of all nations promise to be *loyal* to their country. Americans promise loyalty to the U.S. every time they say the Pledge of *Allegiance*. A pledge is a *promise* that people make to America. *Out of respect* for the flag that represents their country, citizens *stand* and place their right hands over their *hearts while* they say the Pledge of Allegiance.

Americans are proud of their form of government. In the Pledge of Allegiance, Americans say that their country is the United States of America. It is a union of many states. It is not a federation of states. It is one nation. Furthermore, citizens say their country is a republic. This means that the government is by the people and for the people. It also means that Americans choose a democratic form of government.

This decision gives them the opportunity to vote for candidates at all levels of government.

The Pledge of Allegiance says that our Union is *indivisible,* which means it cannot be separated. When the southern states tried to separate from the Union, America fought the Civil War. The Pledge of Allegiance also promises that this country is "under God." Many people came to America for religious freedom. They believed that people have the right to religious freedom. The U.S. does not have an official religion. Americans believe that an official religion would conflict with religious freedom.

The last phrase of the Pledge of Allegiance — with liberty and justice for all — is one reason millions of immigrants came to America. They wanted liberty and justice. The fight for liberty and justice for everyone continues even today. Americans pledge allegiance to the flag. They pledge liberty and justice for all. It is everyone's responsibility to make these promises true.

Activity Section

Activity 1
Read each sentence. Write an affirmative sentence to say what is correct.

1. The Pledge of Allegiance is not a promise.

   The Pledge of Allegiance is a promise.

2. Americans do not pledge allegiance to the flag.

   _____

3. The United States is not one nation.

   _____

4. Liberty and justice are not for all.

   _____

5. Americans are not proud of their form of government.

   _____

6. The United States is not a republic.

   _____

7. In the U.S., government is not by the people and for the people.

   _____

8. Americans don't have a democratic form of government.

   _____

Activity 2

Write the number of the correct answer in the blank.

1. What is a pledge?

2. To what do we pledge allegiance?

3. Is the U.S. a federation of states?

4. Is there an official religion in the U.S.?

5. What is the last line of the Pledge of Allegiance?

6. How does the Pledge of Allegiance begin?

_____ No, it is not.

_____ No, there is not.

_____ ". . . with liberty and justice for all."

_____ "I pledge allegiance to the flag . . ."

_____ to the flag

_____ It is a promise.

Quiz

Write <u>true</u> or <u>false</u> after each sentence.

1. People place their right hands over their hearts to say the Pledge of Allegiance. _____

2. The Pledge of Allegiance is a promise. _____

3. The U.S. has a republican form of government. _____

4. The U.S. is many nations. _____

5. The fight for liberty and justice is over. _____

6. The Pledge of Allegiance says the U.S. is not indivisible. _____

Lesson 29
The Capital

Competency Objectives
After completing Lesson 29, students will be able to **(1)** identify and locate the capital of the United States on a map and **(2)** indicate the location of the White House.

Washington, D.C. (District of Columbia), is the capital of the United States. It is there that the federal government has many of its offices.

Washington, D.C., does not belong to any state. It is not a state; it is a district. It is between the states of Maryland and Virginia. It covers only 67 *square miles*. The streets look like *spokes* of a wheel. They divide the city into 4 different geographic areas. Look at the map of the U.S. in the Appendix. Find Washington, D.C.

There are many government buildings in Washington, D.C. The Senate and the House of Representatives meet in the Capitol to make laws. The Supreme Court meets in the Supreme Court Building to explain laws and hear court cases. The President lives in the White House on Pennsylvania Avenue.

The center of the capital has many beautiful monuments. It has the Washington Monument, the Jefferson Memorial, the Lincoln Memorial, and many others to *remind* us of our heroes. Japan *gave* the city beautiful cherry trees that *bloom* in the spring. These trees add to the beauty of the city.

Activity Section

Activity 1 (pair work)

Practice the dialogue with another student.

S-1:   What is Washington, D.C.?

S-2:   It is the capital of the U.S.

S-1:   What does D.C. mean?

S-2:   It means District of Columbia.

S-1:   Is it a part of Maryland?

S-2:   No. It doesn't belong to any state.

Activity 2

Read each sentence. Write an affirmative sentence to say what is correct.

1. Washington, D.C., is not between Maryland and Virginia.

_____

2. Washington, D.C., does not cover 67 square miles.

_____

3. The Senate and the House do not meet in the Capitol.

_____

4. The Supreme Court does not explain laws.

_____

5. The White House is not on Pennsylvania Avenue.

_____

6. Washington, D.C., does not have many monuments.

_____

7. There isn't a Washington Monument in Washington, D.C.

_____

Activity 3

Circle the correct response.

1. The capital of the U.S. is between _____ .
   a. Maryland and Virginia　　　　b. Arizona and Washington

2. The capital of the U.S. is a _____ .
   a. state　　　　　　　　　　　b. district

3. The city of Washington, D.C., is _____ .
   a. very big　　　　　　　　　　b. very small

4. Washington, D.C., has _____ monuments.
   a. many　　　　　　　　　　　b. few

5. Japan gave the city _____ .
   a. a monument　　　　　　　　b. cherry trees

Quiz

Answer the following questions. Use short or complete answers.

1. Who lives at the White House?

_____

2. How big is the District of Columbia?

_____

3. The White House is on an avenue. Which avenue?

_____

4. Washington, D.C., is near Virginia. What other state is it near?

_____

5. Where does the Supreme Court meet?

_____

Lesson 30
State and Local Government

Competency Objectives
After completing Lesson 30, students will be able to
(1) identify 3 levels of government, **(2)** state the branches of
state government, and **(3)** identify counties and cities as
subdivisions of states.

Government is the administration and control of public *policy*. In the U.S., there is a federal government and there are state and local governments.

The federal government is the largest body of government. It *plans* and *does* business for the *entire* country. The Constitution *states* the responsibility and *structure* of the federal government. Any power that the Constitution does not give to the federal government belongs to the states. The federal government is larger now than in 1787, but the *basic* laws of government are the same. The structure of government is the same. The branches of government are still the executive, the legislative, and the judicial branches. Each branch has *specific* functions.

In 1787, the United States had only 13 states. Today there are 50 states in the U.S. The founding fathers *planned* for more states to join the Union. They wanted the new states to have the same type of government as the original states.

Every state government has a constitution. That constitution cannot disagree with the Constitution of the U.S. Every state government also has 3 branches: the executive, the legislative, and the judicial.

Laws *passed* by states cannot disagree with the federal Constitution. Moreover, state laws apply only to the people that live in that state. Every state has the responsibility to protect the lives of the people in that state. The state is responsible for transportation, education, and the laws of business in that state. The state and federal governments work together in many areas. *Housing* and health care are 2 of those areas.

States have *subdivisions,* or smaller areas. Counties are subdivisions of states. Counties have charters. These charters indicate how the government of the county functions. They also indicate what officials people may elect to run the government. County charters cannot disagree with state constitutions or the U.S. Constitution. County government runs programs at the local level. County and state work together in many areas. Transportation and *safety* are 2 of those areas.

The smallest unit of government is city or municipal government. There are usually many cities in a county. Counties give some money from taxes to cities. Cities also collect taxes from local people. These taxes pay for police, fire departments, parks, and other services. City government is the *closest* form of government to the individual citizen. Citizens have a more immediate voice in city government because city halls are usually close to where they live.

Activity Section

Activity 1

Complete each sentence with the correct information.

1. The 3 levels of government are federal, _____, and local.

2. The _____ government is the largest body of government.

3. The smallest unit of government is city or _____ government.

4. State constitutions cannot _____ the U.S. Constitution.

5. _____ are subdivisions of states.

Activity 2

Practice these sentences.

1. How many **states** are in **the U.S.?**

        counties   your state
        cities   your county

2. **The U.S.** has a **constitution?**

   Every state   constitution
   Every county charter
   Every city   local government

3. The **federal** government helps **state** governments.

     state   county
     county   local

Activity 3

Write <u>true</u> or <u>false</u> after each sentence.

1. Every state has 3 branches of government. _____

2. Citizens pay taxes to local governments. _____

3. The basic laws of the U.S. government are the same as in 1787. _____

4. The U.S. has 13 states now. _____

5. The federal government is responsible for education in each state. _____

6. The state and the federal governments never work together. _____

Quiz

Circle the correct response.

1. There are _____ levels of government in the U.S.
   a. 4   b. 2   c. 3

2. State government has _____ branches.
   a. 4   b. 3   c. 2

3. _____ are subdivisions of a state.
   a. Towns and countries   b. Counties and cities   c. Police and fire departments

4. Citizens _____ taxes.
   a. pay   b. do not pay   c. buy

Lesson 31
Residency Requirements

Competency Objectives
After completing Lesson 31, students will be able to **(1)** state the process and basic requirements to become a permanent resident and **(2)** fill out a change of address form.

After you become a temporary resident, the Immigration office sends you a *notice*. This notice *tells* you what you must do.

As a temporary resident, you *must live* in the United States continuously for 2½ years. That means *all the time,* with only short visits outside of the country. You may leave the U.S. for short visits of less than 30 days. The total number of short visits *cannot be* more than 90 days. The Immigration office counts those days from the time you become a temporary resident until you become a permanent resident. If a temporary resident *moves,* he or she must *fill out* a Change of Address Card for Legalization and Special Agricultural Workers. The number of the form is I-697. Only ELA and SAW applicants with temporary residence may use this form.

You can get a change of address form from the Legalization Office where you filed your application. This is **NOT** the Post Office change of address card. Some agencies or schools may also have this form.

Mail this card to the same office where you filed for temporary residency. Place a 15-cent stamp on the card.

To be a permanent resident:
1. You must demonstrate a *minimal understanding* of ordinary English. That means you must answer simple questions such as "Where do you work?" or "What is your alien registration number?"
2. You must know and understand basic facts about U.S. history and government. You can find these facts in this book.
3. You must be *"satisfactorily pursuing"* a course of study to achieve these skills. Pursuing means to begin, follow, and continue. Satisfactorily means to attend class and continue until the skills needed are met.

You must be a temporary resident for 18 months before you can apply for permanent residency. After that time, you have 1 year to become a permanent resident. If you do not apply, you may *lose* your permission to stay in the U.S.

Activity Section

Activity 1
Circle the correct response.

1. Temporary residents must live in the U.S. for _____ years continuously.
   a. 1½   b. 2½   c. 3½

2. The total number of short visits may be _____.
   a. 91 days   b. 90 days   c. more than 90 days

3. Temporary residents who move must fill out _____ form.
   a. an application   b. a change of address   c. a legalization form

4. To be a permanent resident, you must learn some _____.
   a. Spanish   b. mathematics   c. English

5. Temporary residents have _____ to fulfill requirements to be permanent residents.
   a. 1 year   b. 1½ years   c. 2 years

Activity 2 (pair or group work)
Ask a classmate the following questions. Then write the answers.

1. You are a temporary resident. You want to become a permanent resident. How much time do you have?

   _____

2. How long must temporary residents live in the U.S. continuously?

   _____

3. Who may use the I-697 form?

   _____

4. Look at the I-697 form in this lesson. What does SAW mean?

   _____

5. What is your date of birth?

   _____

Activity 3

Practice filling out this form.

U.S. Department of Justice Immigration and Naturalization Service	**Change of Address Card for Legalization and Special Agricultural Workers (SAW)**

INSTRUCTIONS: This form is to be used ONLY by Legalization and SAW applicants (in connection with an application for status under Sec. 245A or Sec. 210 of the Immigration and Nationality Act) reporting a change of address. Mail to the Legalization Office where your application was submitted.

Name (Last in CAPS)	(First)	(Middle)
Country of Birth	**Date of Birth** (Month/Day/Year)	**A–File No:**
Present Address (Street or Rural Route)	(City or Post Office)	(State and ZIP Code)

IF ABOVE ADDRESS IS TEMPORARY I expect to remain there _____ years _____ months.

Last Address (Street or Rural Route)	(City or Post Office)	(State and ZIP Code)
SIGNATURE	**DATE**	

Quiz

Write <u>true</u> or <u>false</u> after each sentence.

1. To become a permanent resident, you must learn a little English. _____

2. To become a permanent resident, you must understand basic facts about U.S history and government. _____

3. To become a permanent resident, you must leave the U.S. for 95 days. _____

4. ELA means Eligible Legalization Alien. _____

5. Temporary residents don't need change of address forms if they move. _____

Lesson 32
Eligible Legal Aliens

Competency Objectives
After completing Lesson 32, students will be able to **(1)** discuss rules that apply to work permits, **(2)** discuss the rules of receiving welfare, and **(3)** identify felonies and misdemeanors.

Eligible Legalization Aliens (ELAs) are temporary residents. Temporary residents need a work permit to work legally in the U.S.

As a temporary resident, you get a work permit when you complete your first interview successfully. When that happens, the INS gives you a receipt with your identification number. Later, you *will receive* an identification card by mail. The identification card has your alien registration number. The identification card also has the date it *was issued.* Use your receipt until the INS sends your card.

As a temporary resident, you need an alien registration card to work legally. You must carry this card at all times. You also need a social security card to work. The Social Security Administration Office in your area *issues* that card. To get a card, you need proof of your birth date. You also need your alien registration card or the receipt from the Legalization Office of Immigration.

As an Eligible Legalization Alien, you must not receive certain types of welfare — *particularly* cash assistance. Some aliens may receive a *public charge waiver* when they apply. If you do so, you must *prove* that you did not receive any benefits illegally.

You must respect the laws of the U.S. if you want to live in this country. If you commit a felony, the INS may not give you permanent residency. A felony is a major crime *such as murder,* burglary, or rape. You must not be arrested for more than 3 misdemeanors. A misdemeanor is an *offense* less serious than a felony.

Temporary residents who *obey* the law and *stay out of trouble* do not have to *worry.*

Activity Section

Activity 1

Practice these sentences.

1. Temporary residents need **work permits.**

                                    an identification card
                                    a Social Security card
                                    proof of birth

2. **A felony** is a major crime.

    Burglary
    Murder
    Rape

3. You must **respect the laws.**

                  get a work permit
                  get an identification card
                  complete an interview

4. Temporary residents need **work permits.**

                                      identification cards
                                      Social Security cards
                                    proof of birth date

Activity 2

Write <u>true</u> or <u>false</u> after each sentence.

1. Temporary residents need work permits. _____

2. Temporary residents must complete an interview. _____

3. Residents do not need an alien registration number. _____

4. Temporary residents must not receive certain types of welfare. _____

5. Only legal aliens must obey the laws. _____

Quiz

Circle the correct response.

1. ELAs are _____ residents.

   a. permanent   b. temporary

2. You _____ an alien registration number to work legally.

   a. need   b. do not need

3. You _____ a Social Security card.

   a. do not need   b. need

4. Rape _____ a felony.

   a. is   b. is not

5. A felony _____ a major crime.

   a. is not   b. is

Lesson 33
On Becoming a Citizen

Competency Objectives

After completing Lesson 33, students will be able to **(1)** state the basic requirements to become a U.S. citizen and **(2)** identify required documents for citizenship.

After 5 years of permanent *residency,* a resident who is at least 18 years old can apply for citizenship. There are a few other requirements. To become a citizen, a person must do the following:

- Learn to speak, read, and write English
- Learn to *sign* his or her name in English
- Learn some U.S. history and government
- Live in the U.S. 6 months continuously *before* he or she applies
- Be of good moral character
- Be loyal to the United States

Every new citizen takes the *oath* of allegiance to the U.S. on the day that he or she becomes a citizen. The process to become a citizen is *simple. Applicants* must do the following:

1. *File* an application
2. Pass an examination
3. Go to a hearing

Residents can get an application at any immigration office. They must do the following:

1. Fill out the application truthfully
2. Complete the biography sheet with correct information

3. Include a fingerprint chart
4. Include 2 unsigned photographs

Police stations and other *qualified* persons take fingerprints.

The INS also requires proof of identification and other important documents such as the following:

- Alien registration card and receipt
- Passport
- Marriage *certificate* and children's *birth* certificates
- Any record of driving tickets

The Immigration and Naturalization Service reviews the application and the documents. If everything is correct and complete, the INS sets a date for an interview. At the interview, the officer asks about information on the application. The officer also helps applicants file the Petition for Naturalization. The officer asks the applicant some simple questions about the American government and the history of the United States. Applicants must pass a short oral test in English and write a simple dictation. Applicants must also be able to sign their names. People who are over 50 years old or who have been residents for more than 20 years do not take the literacy test.

After the examination, the INS official *files* the Petition for Naturalization. The resident goes to a final court hearing before a judge. The officer may or may not recommend the person for citizenship. If the officer recommends a resident for citizenship, the INS judge sets a *date* for the *swearing-in ceremony*. At this ceremony, the resident takes the oath to be loyal to the U.S. The resident also *swears* to defend the U.S. At the ceremony, the judge gives each new citizen a certificate of naturalization.

The new naturalized citizen has the rights and responsibilities of any other American citizen. Citizens have the right and the responsibility to vote. The naturalized citizen can run for any office except President or Vice President. If the person wants a job on certain federal projects, he or she must get a *security clearance*. Citizens can enter and *leave* the country at any time. They travel with an American passport. More important for many naturalized citizens is the fact that they may help other immediate members of their families migrate to the U.S.

Activity Section

Activity 1
Circle the correct response.

1. New citizens _____ an oath of allegiance.
   a. take   b. do not take

2. Applicants must fill out an application with _____.
   a. false information   b. the truth

3. Applicants for citizenship _____ a fingerprint chart.
   a. do not need   b. need

4. The INS officer _____ recommend the candidate for citizenship.
   a. may or may not   b. must

5. Residents _____ the right to vote.
   a. have   b. do not have

Activity 2

Write true or false after each sentence.

1. After 3 years of residency, any resident can become a citizen. _____

2. A person must be at least 16 years old to become a citizen. _____

3. You must learn to speak, read, and write English to become a citizen. _____

4. Applicants do not have to pass a test for citizenship. _____

5. INS means International Service. _____

Activity 3

Read each sentence. Write an affirmative sentence to say what is correct.

1. Naturalized citizens cannot be senators.

_____

2. There is not a test for applicants for citizenship.

_____

3. New citizens do not swear to be loyal and to defend the U.S.

_____

4. Applicants for citizenship under 50 years old do not take a literacy test.

_____

Quiz

Write true or false after each sentence.

1. You must be at least 18 years old to apply for citizenship. _____

2. You must be of good moral character to apply for citizenship. _____

3. Applicants file a Petition of Naturalization to become a citizen. _____

4. Applicants for citizenship must go to a hearing. _____

5. Residents can get an application at any INS office. _____

Lesson 34
The State of California

Competency Objectives

After completing Lesson 34, students will be able to
(1) identify California as the third largest state in the U.S.,
(2) identify the California flag, and **(3)** identify what borders
California.

The state of California is the third largest state in the Union. It has a land area of 155,562 square miles. The Pacific Ocean is the western border of California. The state of Oregon is to the north of California. The states of Nevada and Arizona are to the east, and Mexico is to the south. California has the largest population in the United States. The population of California was 23,668,562 in 1980. It is more today. There are 58 counties in the state.

Every state has a flag. The official flag of California is the Bear Flag. It has a large grizzly bear and a red star on a white *background*. The flag also has a red stripe across the bottom of the flag.

California has 2 senators. Alan Cranston is a Democrat. He became a senator in 1968. He was reelected in 1974, 1980, and 1986. Pete Wilson, the other senator in 1988, is a Republican. These senators represent the entire state.

California has 45 members in the House of Representatives. In 1988, 27 representatives were Democrats and 18 were Republicans.

All elected officials in California serve 4-year terms. There is no limit on the number of terms they may serve. The governor is an elected official. To be governor of California, a person must be a citizen of the United States. The governor must be a resident of California for at least 5 years before the election. He or she must be at least 18 years old. The governor is the highest officer in the state.

California also has a lieutenant governor. The people elect the lieutenant governor. Qualifications for lieutenant governor are the same as for governor. The lieutenant governor acts as governor when the governor leaves the state.

Activity Section

Activity 1
Write <u>true</u> or <u>false</u> after each sentence.

1. California is the largest state in size in the nation. _____

2. Oregon is west of California. _____

3. Nevada and Arizona are south of California. _____

4. California has 48 counties. _____

5. California has 48 members in the House of Representatives. _____

Activity 2
Ask a classmate the following questions. Then write the answers.

1. Who is the highest officer in the state of California?

   _____

2. What is the third largest state in the nation?

   _____

3. What is the official flag of California?

   _____

4. Mexico is south of California. Where is Oregon?

   _____

5. How many California representatives are in the House?

   _____

Quiz

Circle the correct response.

1. California is the _____ state in population in the nation.
   a. largest   b. second largest   c. third largest

2. The lieutenant governor is _____.
   a. appointed   b. elected   c. selected

3. The California flag has _____.
   a. 1 star   b. 48 stars   c. no star

4. The Pacific Ocean is _____ of California.
   a. east   b. west   c. north

5. _____ is south of California.
   a. Canada   b. Oregon   c. Mexico

Lesson 35
Plan of Government for California

Competency Objectives

After completing Lesson 35, students will be able to
(1) identify the branches of government in California,
(2) state what each branch does, and **(3)** identify courts in the judicial branch.

Citizens wrote the constitution of California in 1849. California became the 31st state in September of 1850. Citizens rewrote the constitution of California in 1879. Representatives adopted it in Sacramento on March 3, 1879.

The constitution of California is the highest law of the state. It is the plan of the state government. The constitution divides government into 3 branches: legislative, executive, and judicial.

The state legislature makes the laws for the state. The legislature has 2 parts: the senate and the assembly. Eligible voters elect 40 state senators and 80 members to the assembly.

To be a state senator, a person must be at least 18 years old and be a citizen of the U.S. A senator must also be a resident of California for at least 3 years. A senator must be a resident of the district he or she represents at least 30 days before the election. The qualifications for assembly members are the same. Every 2 years there are elections for assembly members. Every 4 years there are elections for senators. A bill must pass the senate and the assembly to become law. The executive branch of California enforces the laws of the state. The governor is the supreme executive officer of the state. The following are a few of the governor's responsibilities:

- Presents a budget
- Signs or vetoes bills
- Acts as the commander in chief of the state National Guard
- Appoints public officials that are not elected
- Appoints judges to the California Supreme Court
- Appoints a new U.S. senator (if a senator dies)
- Pardons or shortens sentences

The lieutenant governor acts as governor when the governor leaves the state. The lieutenant governor also presides over the senate. He or she serves on certain boards and commissions.

The judicial branch of the state explains the laws of California. The California Constitution provides for 2 types of courts: trial courts and appellate courts. The trial courts are the lower courts. The superior, municipal, and justice courts are trial courts. Cases begin at this level. People may appeal cases to the court of appeals, and then to the state supreme court. The courts of appeal have 6 districts:

1st district San Francisco
2nd district Los Angeles
3rd district Sacramento
4th district San Diego
5th district Fresno
6th district San Jose

There are 58 California trial courts, one in each county. In 1985, there were 677 judges in the trial court system. Trial courts or superior courts try the following types of cases:

Civil — over $25,000
Criminal — all cases *except* those that by law go to municipal or justice courts
Juvenile — cases concerning persons under 18 years old
Appeals — cases that go to the court of appeal of a district

Municipal courts are for places with population over 40,000. Justice courts are for places with population under 40,000. Both courts try the following types of cases:

Civil — $25,000 or less
Small claims — $1,500 or less
Criminal — misdemeanors and infractions
Appeals — to appeals department of the superior court

The governor appoints judges to the state supreme court and the appeals courts initially. After the term of appointment, they must run for reelection.

Activity Section

Activity 1

Match the two columns to complete each sentence.

1. The governor of California   _____ explains laws.

2. The state legislature   _____ presides over the senate.

3. The lieutenant governor   _____ presents budgets.

4. Trial courts   _____ makes laws.

5. The judicial branch   _____ are superior courts.

6. People may appeal cases   _____ to the court of appeals.

Activity 2 (pair or group work)

Read each sentence. Write an affirmative sentence to say what is correct.

1. Citizens did not write the constitution of California in 1849.

   _____

2. Citizens did not rewrite the constitution of California in 1879.

   _____

3. The constitution of California is not the highest law of the state.

   _____

4. California does not have 3 branches of government.

   _____

5. Senators are not residents of California.

   _____

6. We do not elect assembly members in California every 2 years.

   _____

7. We do not elect senators in California every 4 years.

   _____

Quiz

Write true or false after each sentence.

1. California has 3 branches of government. _____

2. The legislative branch explains the laws. _____

3. There are 40 members in the California Assembly. _____

4. The superior court is the only court in California. _____

5. The lieutenant governor is appointed. _____

Lesson 36
The New President

Competency Objectives

After completing Lesson 36, students will be able to (1) state simple facts about the 41st President of the U.S. and (2) identify the process to elect a U.S. President.

The President of the United States is the head of the executive branch. The executive branch enforces the laws of the U.S. The President leads the country. The President *directs* the federal government. The President and his men/women enforce federal laws.

Every 4 years there is a presidential election. Political *parties* choose presidential candidates for the elections. To choose their candidates, political parties have *conventions* in every state. Members of each party vote for the candidate they prefer. Each party has a national convention to select candidates for President and Vice President. The 2 major parties are Democratic and Republican. In 1988, there was another presidential election. Citizens chose George Herbert Bush as the 41st President of the U.S. Bush took office in January, 1989. Bush will serve from 1989 to 1993. President Bush is a Republican.

George H. Bush was born in Milton, Massachusetts, on June 12, 1924. He grew up in Massachusetts. He attended school there. Bush served as a pilot in the navy. After his service in the navy, Bush attended Yale University.

George Bush served 2 terms as a U.S. Representative from the 7th district in Texas. He was the U.S. Ambassador to the United Nations at *one time*. He was also the Director of the Central Intelligence Agency (CIA). Bush was Vice President under Ronald Reagan. He was Vice President when he ran for the office of President.

President Bush has to make many important decisions. He has to select a Cabinet. He has to select the head of independent agencies. He has to choose ambassadors to other nations.

Activity Section

Activity 1

Match the two columns to complete each sentence.

1. The President of the U.S. _____ are Democratic and Republican.

2. There is a presidential election _____ their candidates.

3. Political parties have national _____ voted for a President and a Vice President.

4. Members of each party choose _____ office in 1989.

5. The President directs _____ is the head of the executive branch.

6. The two major parties _____ the federal government.

7. Citizens _____ conventions to choose presidential candidates.

8. The new President took _____ every 4 years.

Activity 2

Circle the correct response.

1. Citizens elected the _____ President in 1988.
   a. 40th   b. 41st   c. 39th

2. Political parties choose presidential candidates _____.
   a. at national conventions   b. in Atlanta   c. at county conventions

3. The next presidential election is in _____.
   a. 1990   b. 1992   c. 1997

4. The President and his men/women _____.
   a. enforce the laws   b. pass the laws   c. explain the laws

5. The President works in the _____.
   a. legislative branch   b. executive branch   c. judicial branch

Quiz

Answer the following questions. Use short or complete answers.

1. Who is the 41st President of the U.S.?

_____

2. Who selects presidential candidates?

_____

3. What are the 2 major political parties?

_____

4. Who was the Democratic candidate in 1988?

_____

5. In what year is the next presidential election?

_____

Appendix 1
Map of the World

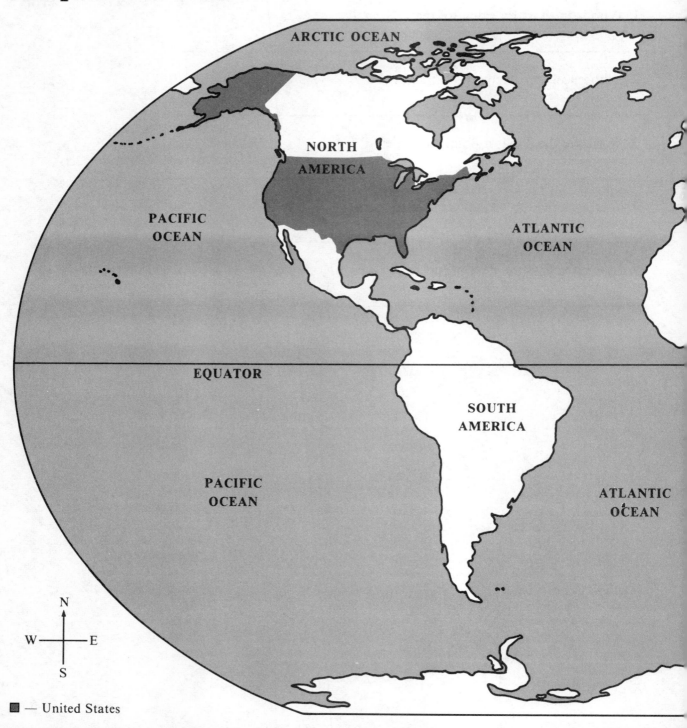

ARCTIC OCEAN

NORTH AMERICA

PACIFIC OCEAN

ATLANTIC OCEAN

EQUATOR

SOUTH AMERICA

PACIFIC OCEAN

ATLANTIC OCEAN

N

W — E

S

■ — United States

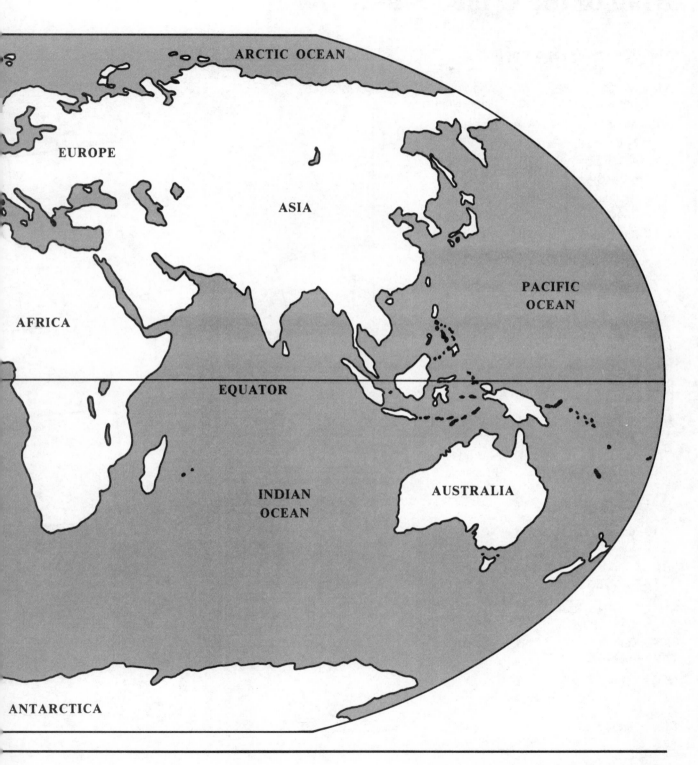

ARCTIC OCEAN

EUROPE

ASIA

AFRICA

PACIFIC
OCEAN

EQUATOR

INDIAN
OCEAN

AUSTRALIA

ANTARCTICA

Appendix 2
Map of the United States

Map Key: States and Capitals

AK—Alaska
  Juneau

AL—Alabama
  Montgomery

AR—Arkansas
  Little Rock

AZ—Arizona
  Phoenix

CA—California
  Sacramento

CO—Colorado
  Denver

CT—Connecticut
  Hartford

DE—Delaware
  Dover

FL—Florida
  Tallahassee

GA—Georgia
  Atlanta

HI—Hawaii
  Honolulu

IA—Iowa
  Des Moines

ID—Idaho
  Boise

IL—Illinois
  Springfield

IN—Indiana
  Indianapolis

KS—Kansas
  Topeka

KY—Kentucky
  Frankfort

LA—Louisiana
  Baton Rouge

MA—Massachusetts
  Boston

MD—Maryland
  Annapolis

ME —Maine
  Augusta

MI —Michigan
  Lansing

MN—Minnesota
  St. Paul

MO—Missouri
  Jefferson City

MS—Mississippi
  Jackson

MT—Montana
  Helena

NC—North Carolina
  Raleigh

ND—North Dakota
  Bismarck

NE—Nebraska
  Lincoln

NH —New Hampshire
  Concord

NJ —New Jersey
  Trenton

NM—New Mexico
  Santa Fe

NV—Nevada
  Carson City

NY—New York
  Albany

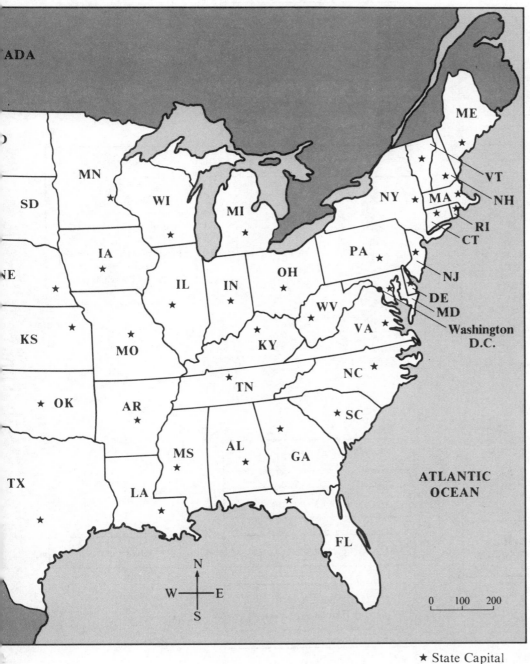

OH—Ohio
Columbus

OK—Oklahoma
Oklahoma City

OR—Oregon
Salem

PA—Pennsylvania
Harrisburg

RI —Rhode Island
Providence

SC—South Carolina
Columbia

SD—South Dakota
Pierre

TN—Tennessee
Nashville

TX—Texas
Austin

UT—Utah
Salt Lake City

VA —Virginia
Richmond

VT —Vermont
Montpelier

WA—Washington
Olympia

WI —Wisconsin
Madison

WV—West Virginia
Charleston

WY—Wyoming
Cheyenne

★ State Capital

Appendix 3
Structure of the U.S. Government

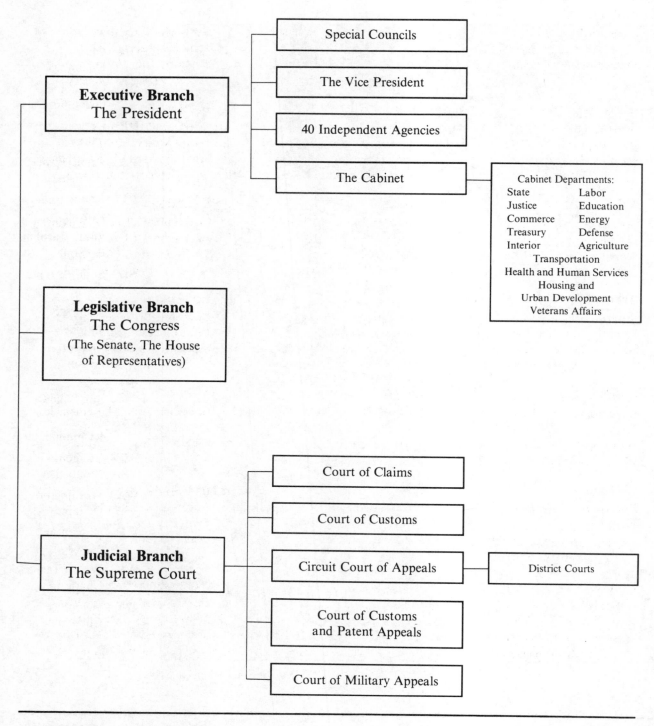

Executive Branch
The President

- Special Councils
- The Vice President
- 40 Independent Agencies
- The Cabinet

Cabinet Departments:

State	Labor
Justice	Education
Commerce	Energy
Treasury	Defense
Interior	Agriculture

Transportation
Health and Human Services
Housing and
Urban Development
Veterans Affairs

Legislative Branch
The Congress
(The Senate, The House
of Representatives)

Judicial Branch
The Supreme Court

- Court of Claims
- Court of Customs
- Circuit Court of Appeals — District Courts
- Court of Customs
  and Patent Appeals
- Court of Military Appeals

Appendix 4
Governors and Senators

Alabama
Governor: Guy Hunt
Term Expires: Jan. 1991
Senators: Howell Heflin
    Richard C. Shelby

Alaska
Governor: Steve Cowper
Term Expires: Dec. 1990
Senators: Ted Stevens
    Frank Murkowski

Arizona
Governor: Rose Mofford
Term Expires: Jan. 1991
Senators: Dennis DeConcini
    John McCain

Arkansas
Governor: Bill Clinton
Term Expires: Jan. 1991
Senators: David Pryor
    Dale Bumpers

California
Governor: George Deukmejian
Term Expires: Jan. 1991
Senators: Pete Wilson
    Alan Cranston

Colorado
Governor: Roy Romer
Term Expires: Jan. 1991
Senators: William L. Armstrong
    Timothy E. Wirth

Connecticut
Governor: William O'Neill
Term Expires: Jan. 1991
Senators: J. I. Lieberman
    Christopher J. Dodd

Delaware
Governor: Michael N. Castle
Term Expires: Jan. 1993
Senators: William V. Roth
    Joseph R. Biden

Florida
Governor: Bob Martinez
Term Expires: Jan. 1991
Senators: Lawton Chiles
    Bob Graham

Georgia
Governor: Joe Frank Harris
Term Expires: Jan. 1991
Senators: Sam Nunn
    Wiche Fowler, Jr.

Hawaii
Governor: John Waihea
Term Expires: Dec. 1990
Senators: Spark M. Matsunaga
    Daniel K. Inouye

Idaho
Governor: Cecil D. Andrus
Term Expires: Jan. 1991
Senators: James A. McClure
    Steven D. Symms

Illinois
Governor: James R. Thompson
Term Expires: Jan. 1991
Senators: Paul Simon
    Alan J. Dixon

Indiana
Governor: Evan Bayh
Term Expires: Jan. 1993
Senators: Richard G. Luger
    Daniel R. Coats

Iowa
Governor: Terry Branstad
Term Expires: Jan. 1991
Senators: Tom Harkin
    Charles Grassley

Kansas
Governor: Mike Hayden
Term Expires: Jan. 1991
Senators: Nancy L. Kassebaum
    Robert J. Dole

Kentucky
Governor: Wallace G. Wilkinson
Term Expires: Jan. 1991
Senators: Mitch McConneli
    Wendell H. Ford

Louisiana
Governor: Buddy Roemer
Term Expires: Jan. 1992
Senators: J. Bennett Johnston
    John B. Breaux

Maine
Governor: John McKeman, Jr.
Term Expires: Jan. 1991
Senators: George J. Mitchell
    William S. Cohen

Maryland
Governor: William D. Schaefer
Term Expires: Jan. 1991
Senators: Paul S. Sarbanes
    Barbara A. Mikuiski

Massachusetts
Governor: Michael S. Dukakis
Term Expires: Jan. 1991
Senators: Edward M. Kennedy
    John Kerry

Michigan

Governor: James J. Blanchard
Term Expires: Jan. 1991
Senators: Donald W. Reigle
　　　　Carl Levin

Minnesota

Governor: Rudy Perpich
Term Expires: Jan. 1991
Senators: David Durenberger
　　　　Rudolph E. Boschwitz

Mississippi

Governor: Ray Mabus
Term Expires: Jan. 1992
Senators: Trent Lott
　　　　Thed Cochran

Missouri

Governor: John D. Ashcroft
Term Expires: Jan. 1993
Senators: John C. Danforth
　　　　Christopher Bond

Montana

Governor: Stanley Stephens
Term Expires: Jan. 1993
Senators: Conrad Burns
　　　　Max Baucus

Nebraska

Governor: Kay Orr
Term Expires: Jan. 1991
Senators: Robert Kerrey
　　　　J. James Exon

Nevada

Governor: Richard Bryan
Term Expires: Jan. 1991
Senators: Richard H. Bryan
　　　　Harry M. Reid

New Hampshire

Governor: Judd A. Gregg
Term Expires: Jan. 1993
Senators: Gordon J. Humphrey
　　　　Warren Rudman

New Jersey

Governor: Thomas H. Kean
Term Expires: Jan. 1990
Senators: Frank Lautenberg
　　　　Bill Bradley

New Mexico

Governor: Garrey E. Carruthers
Term Expires: Jan. 1991
Senators: Jeff Bingaman
　　　　Pete V. Domenici

New York

Governor: Mario M. Cuomo
Term Expires: Jan. 1991
Senators: D. P. Moynihan
　　　　Alfonse D'Amato

North Carolina

Governor: James G. Martin
Term Expires: Jan. 1993
Senators: Jesse Helms
　　　　Terry Sanford

North Dakota

Governor: George A. Sinner
Term Expires: Jan. 1993
Senators: Quentin N. Burdick
　　　　Kent Conrad

Ohio

Governor: Richard F. Celeste
Term Expires: Jan. 1991
Senators: Howard Metzenbaum
　　　　John Glenn

Oklahoma

Governor: Henry Bellmon
Term Expires: Jan. 1991
Senators: David Boren
　　　　Don Nickles

Oregon

Governor: Neil Goldschmidt
Term Expires: Jan. 1991
Senators: Mark O. Hatfield
　　　　Bob Packwood

Pennsylvania

Governor: Robert Casey
Term Expires: Jan. 1991
Senators: John Heinz
　　　　Arlen Specter

Rhode Island

Governor: Edward DiPrete
Term Expires: Jan. 1993
Senators: John H. Chafee
　　　　Claiborne deB. Pell

South Carolina

Governor: Carroli A. Campbell, Jr.
Term Expires: Jan. 1991
Senators: Strom Thurmond
　　　　Ernest F. Hollings

South Dakota

Governor: George S. Mickelson
Term Expires: Jan. 1991
Senators: Larry Pressier
　　　　Thomas A. Daschle

Tennessee

Governor: Ned Ray McWherter
Term Expires: Jan. 1991
Senators: James R. Sasser
　　　　Albert Gore, Jr.

Washington

Governor: Booth Gardner
Term Expires: Jan. 1993
Senators: Slade Gorton
　　　　Brock Adams

West Virginia

Governor: G. Caperton III
Term Expires: Jan. 1993
Senators: Robert C. Byrd
　　　　Jay Rockefeller

Wisconsin

Governor: Tommy G. Thompson
Term Expires: Jan. 1991
Senators: Herbert Kohl
　　　　Robert W. Kasten

Wyoming

Governor: Mike Sullivan
Term Expires: Jan. 1991
Senators: Malcolm Wallop
　　　　Alan Kool Simpson

Texas

Governor: Bill Clements
Term Expires: Jan. 1991
Senators: Lloyd Bentsen
　　　　Phil Gramm

Utah

Governor: Norman Bangerter
Term Expires: Jan. 1993
Senators: Orrin G. Hatch
　　　　E. J. Garn

Vermont

Governor: Madeleine M. Kunin
Term Expires: Jan. 1993
Senators: J. M. Jeffords
　　　　Patrick J. Leahy

Virginia

Governor: Gerald L. Baliles
Term Expires: Jan. 1990
Senators: Charles S. Robb
　　　　John W. Warner

Appendix 5
Requirements for Permanent Residency

Congratulations. You are a temporary resident. Your next *step* is to become a *lawful* permanent resident.

To become a permanent resident you must

1. Reside in the U.S. continuously

   A *single* absence from the U.S. may not be more than 30 days.

   Total number of absences may not be more than 90 days.

2. Not be *convicted* of a felony or 3 misdemeanors *committed* in the U.S.

3. Not receive certain types of cash *assistance* (welfare)

4. Not be a *public charge*

   If you have a public charge *waiver,* you must prove that you received no benefits since you became a temporary resident.

5. *Demonstrate minimal* understanding of ordinary English

6. Demonstrate minimal *knowledge* of the history and government of the U.S.

7. Satisfactorily *pursue* a recognized course of study

   Your INS Legalization Office can give specific information about recognized courses of study.

Note: The INS will send you an application for permanent residence. This application has instructions on where and how to file. You must be a temporary resident for 18 months. You may apply for permanent residence beginning on the first day of the 19th month. You have one year to submit an application. If you don't apply, you lose your permission to stay in the U.S.

Use the change of address form I-697 to notify the INS of any change of address. You can get an I-697 form from any INS Legalization Office.

Appendix 6
Residency Form

DECLARATION OF INTENDING CITIZEN

**(This declaration is not evidence of lawful
admission for permanent residence)**

(1) My full, true, and correct name is _____

_____(Full, true and correct name, without abbreviation.)_____

(2) Other name(s) used: _____

(3) My present place of residence is _____

_____(Number and street)_____

_____|_____|_____|_____
    (City or Town)   (County)   (State)   (ZIP Code)

(4) Alien Registration Number(s): A - _____

(5) I am an alien residing in the United States who:
    (A) has been lawfully admitted for permanent residence; *or*
    (B) has been granted the status of an alien lawfully admitted for temporary residence under section 245A (a) (1) of the Immigration and Nationality Act; *or*
    (C) has been admitted as a refugee under section 207 of the Immigration and Nationality Act; *or*
    (D) has been granted asylum under section 208 of the Immigration and Nationality Act.

(6) I hereby declare my intention in good faith to become a citizen of the United States.

I do swear (affirm) that the statements I have made and the intention I have expressed in this Declaration of Intending Citizen subscribed by me are true to the best of my knowledge and belief.

_____
(Signature of Declarant)

PENALTIES FOR SUBMITTING FALSE INFORMATION

Federal law provides for imprisonment and/or fine for any false statements made in connection with this Declaration.

Received and filed by

_____ (INS Officer)

at _____ on this _____

day of _____ , 19 _____ .

Appendix 7
Directory of INS Legalization Offices

Alaska
Michael Bldg.
620 E. 10th Ave., Ste. 102
Anchorage, AK 99510

Arizona
3420 S. 7th St.
Phoenix, AZ 85040

4600 S. Park Ave., Ste. 5
Tucson, AZ 85714

281 W. Maley
Willcox, AZ 85643

1325 W. 16th St.
Yuma, AZ 85364

California
1011 17th St.
Bakersfield, CA 93301

9858 Artesia Blvd.
Bellflower, CA 90706

7342 Orangethorpe Ave.
Buena Park, CA 90621

1627 W. Main St.
El Centro, CA 92243

9660 Flair Dr.
El Monte, CA 91731

463 N. Midway Dr.
Escondido, CA 92027

714 4th St.
Eureka, CA 95501

1649 Van Ness Ave.
Fresno, CA 93721

Greenbriar Plaza
12912 Brookhurst Blvd.
Garden Grove, CA 92640

555 Redondo Beach Blvd.
Torrance, CA 90248

California continued
6022 Santa Fe Ave.
Huntington Park, CA 90255

83-558 Ave. 45, Ste. 8
Indio, CA 92201

1671 Wilshire Blvd.
Los Angeles, CA 90017

1241 S. Soto St.
Los Angeles, CA 90022

11307 Vanowen St.
N. Hollywood, CA 91605

100 14th St.
Oakland, CA 94612

400 S. "A" St.
Oxnard, CA 93030

60 E. Holt Ave.
Pomona, CA 91767

1401 Gold St.
Redding, CA 96001

1285 Columbia Ave.
Riverside, CA 92507

3041 65th St.
Sacramento, CA 95820-9000

947 Blanco Circle
Salinas, CA 93901

3247 Mission Village Dr.
San Diego, CA 92123

Appraisers Bldg.
630 Sansome St.
San Francisco, CA 94111

1727 Mission St.
San Francisco, CA 94103-2417

1040 Commercial St.
San Jose, CA 95112

1901 S. Ritchey St.
Santa Ana, CA 99501

California continued
16921 Parthenia St.
Sepulveda, CA 91343

7475 Murray Dr.
Stockton, CA 95210

Colorado
Albrook Center
4730 Paris St.
Denver, CO 80239

Enterprise Bldg.
255 Main St.
Grand Junction, CO 81501

220 S. Victoria St.
Pueblo, CO 81003

Connecticut
414 Chapel St.
New Haven, CT 06511

Florida
799 Galiano St.
Coral Gables, FL 33134

Jackson Bldg.
601 S. Andrews Ave.
Ft. Lauderdale, FL 33301

Palm Springs Mile Mall
500 W. 49th St.
Hialeah, FL 33012

Federal Bldg.
400 W. Bay St.
Jacksonville, FL 32202

Rotunda Plaza
18922 S. Dixie Hwy.
Miami, FL 33157

North Lake Business Park
2900 S.W. 3rd Terrace
Okeechobee, FL 33974

Florida continued

Corporate Square
7402 N. 56th St., Ste. 625
Tampa, FL 33617

Georgia

1395 Columbia Dr., Ste. A-10
Decatur, GA 30032

Guam

801 Pacific News Bldg.
238 O'Hara St.
Agana, GU 96910

Hawaii

1680 Kapiolani Blvd.
Honolulu, HI 96814

Idaho

Stout Bldg. II
1828 Airport Way
Boise, ID 83705

Exchange Plaza Bldg.
1820 E. 17th St.
Idaho Falls, ID 83401

Illinois

Farmsworth Center for Business
1050 Corporate Blvd.
Aurora, IL 60504

3119 N. Pulaski
Chicago, IL 60641

Crown Oaks Midwest
Ground Floor
1700 W. 119th St.
Chicago, IL 60643

Forest Park Mall-Lower Level
7600 W. Roosevelt Rd.
Forest Park, IL 60130

Indiana

College Park Pyramids
3500 DePauw Blvd.
Indianapolis, IN 46268

Iowa

2720 W. Locust St., Ste. 14
Davenport, IA 52804

3619½ Douglas St.
Des Moines, IL 50310

Kansas

Forest Park Bldg.
2506 John St.
Garden City, KS 67846

540 S. Water
Wichita, KS 67202

Louisiana

512 S. Peters
New Orleans, LA 70130

Maine

156 Federal St.
Portland, ME 04101

Maryland

U.S. Appraisers Stores
Gay & Lombard St., 2nd Floor
Baltimore, MD 21202

Massachusetts

600 Washington St.
Boston, MA 02111

1149 Main St.
Springfield, MA 01103

Michigan

15160 W. 8 Mile Rd.
Oak Park, MI 48237

Minnesota

Alpha Business Center
2700 E. 82nd St.
Bloomington, MN 55420

Missouri

3445 Bridgeland Dr., Ste. 123
Bridgeton, MO 63044

10336 N.W. Prairie View Rd.
Kansas City, MO 64153

Montana

Professional Plaza Bldg.
900 N. Montana
Helena, MT 59601

Nebraska

Bennett Bldg.
1437 10th St.
Gering, NE 69341

River City Office Bldg.
399 N. 117th St., Ste. 411
Omaha, NE 68154

New Jersey

30 N. 5th St.
Camden, NJ 08101

2853-2857 J. F. Kennedy Blvd.
Jersey City, NJ 07306

Franklin Mill Office Center
22 Mills St.
Paterson, NJ 07501

New Mexico

1900 Bridge Blvd., S.W.
Albuquerque, NM 87105

Nevada

3055 S. Valley Blvd.
Las Vegas, NV 89102

Nevada continued
350 S. Rock Blvd., Unit B
Reno, NV 89502

New York
Ansonia Center
712 Main St. at Tupper
Buffalo, NY 14202

250 Fulton Ave.
Hempstead, NY 11550

VA Federal Bldg.
201 W. 24th St., 3rd Floor
New York, NY 10001

28-10 Queens Bridge Plaza S.
Long Island City, NY 11101

344 W. Genesee
Syracuse, NY 13202

North Carolina
Highland Park Commerce Center
810 Tyvola Rd., Ste. 132
Charlotte, NC 28217

Ohio
100 E. 8th St.
Cincinnati, OH 45202

A. J. Celebreeze Federal Bldg.
1240 E. 9th St.
Cleveland, OH 44199

Oklahoma
W. Park Business Center
4149 Highline Blvd., Ste. 300
Oklahoma City, OK 73108

Oregon
AT&T Bldg.
202 S.E. Dorion St.
Pendleton, OR 97801

Oregon continued
Federal Bldg.
511 N.W. Broadway
Portland, OR 97209

Pennsylvania
Fair Acres Center
Rt. 352
Lima, PA 19037

Moorehead Federal Bldg.
1000 Liberty Ave., 3rd Fl., Rm. 314
Pittsburgh, PA 15222

Puerto Rico
1609 Ponce De Leon
Santurce, PR 00908

Tennessee
147 Jefferson Ave.
Memphis, TN 38103

Texas
2001 E. Division
Arlington, TX 76011

2800 S. I-25, Ste. 115
Austin, TX 78704

Commerce 2
4410 Dillon Lane
Corpus Christi, TX 78415

Lakeside Shopping Center
7028 Alameda Ave.
El Paso, TX 79915

603 Ed Carey Dr.
Harlingen, TX 78550

2974 Fulton
Houston, TX 77009

2331 Saunders Plaza
Laredo, TX 78043

1940 Ave. "G"
Lubbock, TX 79404

Texas continued
Alta Vista Retail Center
1007 Poteet Jourdanton Freeway
San Antonio, TX 78224

Utah
2990 S. Main St.
Salt Lake City, UT 84115

Vermont
Federal Bldg.
P.O. Box 328
St. Albans, VT 05478

Virginia
1521 N. Danville St., 1st Floor
Arlington, VA 22201

Washington
430 W. Lewis St.
Pasco, WA 99301

815 Airport Way S.
Seattle, WA 98134

Franklin Bldg.
1139 Princeton St.
Wenatchee, WA 98801

INS Bldg.
315 N. 5th Ave.
Yakima, WA 98902

West Virginia
550 Eagan St., Ste. 203
Charleston, WV 25301

Wisconsin
Forest Home Office Bldg.
8405 W. Forest Home Ave.
Greenfield, WI 53228

Appendix 8
Glossary

English Spanish

abolished abolió
accomplishments logros
accused acusado
across a través
added agregó
address discurso
afraid temer
against contra
age edad
aliens extranjeros
alive vivo
all over por todo
all the time continuamente
allegiance lealtad
allows permite
although aunque
amend corregir, rectificar
among entre
angry enojado
anthem himno
anxiously ansiosamente
apparently aparentemente
appeal apelar, apelación
applicants solicitantes
appointments nombramientos
approve aprobar
armed forces fuerzas armadas
assassinated asesinado
assistance asistencia
attacks ataques
attempt intento
attended asistió, asistieron
authority autoridad, jurisdiccion
background fondo, trasfondo
basic básicas, básico
be able poder hacer algo

before antes
begins comienza
believed creían
besides además de
better mejor
bill proyecto de ley
birth nacimiento
bloody sangrienta(o)
bloom en flor, florido
bombed bombardeó
brave valiente(s)
bravely valientemente
breaks descanso
bridges puentes
Britain Gran Bretaña
brought trajo, trajeron
brutal bestial, cruel
built construyó, construyeron
built roads construyeron carreteras
business empresa, negocio
businessmen empresarios, negociantes
can get puede(n) obtener
candidate candidato(a)
cannot be no puede ser
care importarle a uno
carry out llevar a cabo
caused causó
cemeteries cementerios
century siglo
certificate certificado
civil civil
claim apropiar
clearance aprobación
climbed escalaron
closed cerro, cerraron
closest más cercano
cloth tela

English Spanish

coal carbón
colors colores
committed cometieron, cometido
complained se quejaban
conflict conflicto
continued continuaban
continuously continuamente
contradict contradecir
controlled controlaba
conventions convenciones
convicted convicto, declarado culpable
correct corregir, corrigiera
cotton gin desmotadora, despepitadora
courage valentía
craftsmen artesanos
created creó
criminal criminal(es)
crops cultivos
dangerous arriesgado
date fecha
dawn amanecer
debt deuda
declared declaró
delivers entrega
demanded exigió
demonstrate demostrar
destroyed destruyó
dictatorship dictadura
died murió
difficult difícil
directs dirige
disagreed no estaban de acuerdo
does business entrar en arreglos
donated conribuyeron
dressed se vistieron
dropped dejaron caer

earned ganó
easier más fácil
easy fácil
Eastern Hemisphere Hemisferio Oriental
either tampoco
emphasized enfatizó
employees empleados
end finales
enemy camps campamento enemigo
enforces hace cumplir
ensure asegurar
entered formó parte
entire todo, entero
establish establecer
events eventos
except excepto
exciting emocionante
exhibits exhibiciones
explorers exploradores
factories fábricas
fail fracasar
farmers agricultores
fear temor
fight back defenderse
fighting lucha
file presentar
files presenta
fill out llenar
fired despidieron
fireworks fuegos artificiales
fishermen pescadores
fleet escuadra de barcos
followers seguidores
forced obligó
forget olvidar(ía)
formed formó
founded fundó

framers redactores
freed liberaron
friendship amistad
furthermore además
future futuro
gave dio
get rich enriquecerse
gift regalo
gives out reparte
go on picnics merendar en el campo
greatly mucho
greet dar la bienvenida
grew cultivar(on)
guarantees garantías
had to pay tenía(n) que pagar
halfway a medio camino
hamburgers hamburguesas
happiness felicidad
happy feliz
harbor puerto
hated odiaba
health salud
Health and Human Services
  Servicios Humanos y de Salud
hearing audiencia
hearts corazones
held celebró
helped ayudaron
highest supremo
holidays días feriados
honor honra
hot dogs perros calientes
housing vivienda
hungry tener hambre
hunters cazadores
hurt lastimar
impeaches denuncia

imports importaciones
improved mejoró
includes incluye
indivisible indivisible, no se divide
inhale inhalar(on)
insure asegurar
introduces presenta
issues asuntos
items artículos
jobs empleos
joined se unieron
justice justicia
juvenile juvenil
kept conservar(on), lograron
kill rechazar
king rey
knowledge conocimiento
later después, más tarde
lawful legal
lawyer abogado
leave salir
left salió
less menos
libraries bibliotecas
light luz
light bulb bombillo(a) eléctrico(a)
lines línea, fila
lint pelusa
lives vidas
loaded cargado
loaned (lent) prestó
losing perder
lost perdieron
loyal fiel
making money ganar dinero
marched marcharon
mass en masa

English Spanish

meal   comida

measures   unidades de medida

miles   millas

minimal   mínimo(a)

moreover   además

mortgages   hipotecas

most   mayor parte

moved   se movía(n)

movement   movimiento

moves   se mueve

murder   asesinato

must live   debe vivir

negotiated   negoció

New World   Nuevo Mundo

no longer   ya no

nominate   nombrar

nominates   nombra

nomination   nombramiento

Northern Hemisphere   Hemisferio Nórdico

notice   aviso

oath   juramento

obey   respetar

obtained   obtuvo

offense   delito

on their way   encaminado(s)

one time   una época

organized   organizó, organizaron

our   nuestro(a)

out of respect   por respeto

over   finalizado, terminado

over and over   repetidamente

own   adueñarse

owners   dueños, propietarios

parades   desfiles

particularly   especialmente

parties   partidos

passage   pasaje, pasadizo

passed   aprobado

permission   permiso

piece   pieza

planned   hicieron planes

plans   planes

play   tocar un instrumento

policy   política o plan de acción

political freedom   libertad política

positive   positivo(a)

potato salad   ensalada de papas

power   poder

print   imprimir

procedure   procedimiento

process   proceso

profit   ganancia

promise   promesa

promised   prometió

protect   proteger

protected   protegía

prove   probar

proven   probado

public charge   carga publica

punished   castigado

purpose   propósito

pursue   seguir

qualified   calificado, calificadas

quietly   silenciosamente

ratify   aprobar

reacted   reaccionar(on)

ready   listo(a)

reasons   razones

rebuild   reconstruir

reexamine   reexaminar

regulate   reglamentar

religious freedom   libertad religiosa

remembered   recordados

remind   recordar
represents   representar
requirements   requisitos
residency   residencia
respected   respetado
responsibility   responsabilidad
retirement   jubilación
returned   regresó
rewrite   reescribir
right   derecho
rivers   ríos
room   oportunidad
ruled   dominaba
runs   gobierna
safer   más seguro
safety   seguridad
same procedure   mismo procedimiento
sank   hundió
satisfactorily pursuing   seguir satisfactoriamente
saved   salvó
sea   mar
security   seguridad
seemed   parecía
seniority   antigüedad
sent   envió
separate   separado
serious   serio
services   servicios
share   comparte(n)
shares   comparte
ships   barcos
side   costado
sign   firmar
signed   firmó
simple   sencillo
sing   canta
single   soltero

skilled   experimentado(s)
slavery   esclavitud
small business   empresas pequeñas
sold   vendieron
someone   alguien
song   canción
Southern Hemisphere   Hemisferio Meridional
specific   específico
speeches   discursos
speedy   rápido
spokes   rayos
spread   extendido
square   cuadrado, cuadradas
stand   ponerse de pie
stars   estrellas
started   fundaron
states   establece
stay out of trouble   evitar problemas
stays   permanece
step   paso
still   todavía
Stock Market Crash   quiebra de la bolsa de valores
stores   tiendas, almacenes
strengthen   fortalecer
strikes   huelgas
stripes   franjas
structure   estructura
struggle   lucha
subdivisions   sudivisiones
succeed   tener éxito
success   éxito
such as   tal(es) como
suffered   sufrido
sun   sol
surface   superficie
surrender   rendirse
survivors   sobrevivientes

English Spanish

swearing-in ceremony   ceremonia de juramentación
swears   jura
taught   enseñó
taxes   impuestos
tell   indicar, decir
territory   territorio
thanked   dio gracias
Thanksgiving   día de acción de gracias
therefore   por lo tanto
thought   pensó, pensaron
threw   tiraron
tired   cansaba
tobacco   tabaco
torch   antorcha
traces   indicios
Treasury Dept.   Ministerio de Hacienda
treaties   tratados, pactos
truth   verdad
turkey   pavo
understanding   comprensión
unhealthy   insalubre
unjust   injusto
unsafe   peligroso, inseguro
until   hasta
upward   hacia arriba
verdict   veredicto
veto   veto
violently   violentamente
wages   salarios
waiver   renuncia
walkout   paro
war   guerra
was called   fue llamado
was issued   fue emitido

weights   unidades de peso
welfare   asistencia social
Western Hemisphere   Hemisferio Occidental
while   mientras
whole   entero, todo
will receive   recibirá
wind   viento
within   dentro de
without   fuera de
won   ganó
worker   trabajador
working place   lugar de trabajo
worry   preocuparse
wrong   equivocado incorrecto
yet   aun así

Appendix 9
Answer Key

Lesson 1

Activity 1
6
3
1
5
2
4

Activity 2
1. Pacific
2. Canada
3. Mexico
4. Atlantic
5. North America

Activity 3
1. globe, surface map
2. halfway between the North Pole and the South Pole
3. no
4. 4
5. Globes are round and show the whole surface of the earth. Surface maps are flat and can show either the whole world or just part of it.
6. No, there are 4.
7. Northern and Western
8. North America

Quiz
1. continents
2. globe
3. Atlantic Ocean
4. south
5. equator
6. oceans
7. continent

Lesson 2

Activity 1
5
4
6
1
2
7
3

Activity 2
Christopher Columbus
Spain
1492
west
tribes
native Americans
North America

Quiz
1. true
2. false
3. false
4. false
5. true
6. true
7. false
8. true

Lesson 3

Activity 1
1. Amerigo Vespucci
2. Spain, France, England, Portugal
3. Spanish explorers
4. Christian religion
5. English and French explorers

Activity 2
explorers
the land
Spain
missionaries
the Christian religion

Quiz
1. b
2. a
3. b
4. c
5. a

Lesson 4

Activity 2
3
6
1
2
5
7
8
9
4

Quiz
1. false
2. true
3. false
4. true
5. true

Lesson 5

Activity 1
3
6
2
9
4
8
7
5
10
1

Activity 2
1. b
2. a
3. b
4. a
5. a

Quiz
1. colonists
2. king of England
3. no
4. yes
5. no
6. colonists
7. climbed onto an English ship and threw tea over the side
8. Boston Tea Party

Lesson 6

Activity 1
1. 1
2. 4
3. 2
4. 3
5. 5
6. 7
7. 6

Activity 2
1. freedom
2. Jefferson
3. birthday
4. Washington
5. Revolutionary War
6. Declaration

Quiz
1. b
2. b
3. a
4. a
5. b

Lesson 7

Activity 1
1. b
2. b
3. b
4. a
5. b
6. b

Activity 2
1. false
2. false
3. true
4. true
5. true

Quiz
1. A document written by the Continental Congress as the basis of a plan of government.
2. 1787
3. Articles of Confederation
4. to revise the Articles of Confederation
5. a. different interests of states
   b. Most people did not want centralized government.

Lesson 8

Activity 2
6
4
2
5
1
3

Activity 3
1. makes
2. enforces
3. explains

Quiz
1. a
2. b
3. b
4. a
5. b
6. b

Lesson 9

Activity 1
1. b
2. a
3. b
4. b
5. b
6. b
7. a
8. b
9. a
10. a

Quiz
1. false
2. false
3. false
4. true
5. false

Lesson 10

Activity 1
1. executive branch
2. native-born
3. 4 years
4. reelected
5. writes
6. enforces

Quiz
1. b
2. b
3. a
4. a
5. b
6. b

Lesson 11

Activity 1
2
4
5
3
1

Activity 2
1. b
2. a
3. b
4. b
5. a
6. a
7. a
8. b

Quiz
1. the President
2. the 1st President
3. Abraham Lincoln
4. He started the Social Security system. He led the country out of the Depression.
5. yes

Lesson 12

Activity 1
1. a
2. a
3. a
4. a
5. b
6. b

Activity 3
1. 14
2. secretary
3. State, Treasury, Defense, Justice, Interior, Agriculture, Commerce, Labor, Health and Human Services, Housing and Urban Development, Transportation, Education, Energy, or Veterans Affairs
4. Justice
5. U.S. Postal Service, Small Business Administration, or Commission on Civil Rights

Quiz
1. false
2. true
3. true
4. true
5. false

Lesson 13

Activity 1
wanted
equal power
states
legislature
states
protects
dictators
2
in proportion

Activity 2
4
3
1
2
6
5

Quiz
1. b
2. b
3. b
4. a
5. a

Lesson 14

Activity 1
1. c
2. b
3. b
4. a
5. b

Quiz
4. 6 years
5. to make laws

Lesson 15

Activity 1
7
4
5
2
6
8
3
1

Activity 2
1. false
2. true
3. false
4. true
5. false

Quiz
1. b
2. b
3. a
4. b
5. b

Lesson 16

Activity 1
1. false
2. true
3. true
4. true
5. true

Activity 2
1. Congress
2. yes
3. amend, rewrite, kill, send it to its house
4. House of Representatives
5. He can veto bills.

Activity 3
2
3
5
1
6
4

Quiz
1. a
2. a
3. b
4. a
5. b

Lesson 17

Activity 1
1. local
2. judicial
3. justices
4. explains
5. other
6. final

Activity 3
1. the President
2. Congress
3. for life
4. 9
5. appeal
6. Supreme Court

Quiz
1. false
2. true
3. true
4. true
5. false
6. true
7. true

Lesson 18

Activity 1
1. b
2. a
3. a
4. b
5. b
6. b
7. b

Activity 2
1. true
2. false
3. true
4. true
5. false
6. false
7. true
8. true

Quiz
7
4
5
6
3
1
2
8

Lesson 19

Activity 1
difficult
enemy
Confederate Army
brothers
brothers
against
the issue of slavery
economy
right
Union of the U.S.
Abraham Lincoln

Activity 2
2
1
6
7
8
3
9
5
10
4

Quiz
1. b
2. b
3. a
4. b
5. a

Lesson 20

Activity 2
1. false
2. true
3. true
4. true
5. false
6. false
7. false
8. false

Quiz
2
3
4
5
6
1

Lesson 21

Activity 1
1. England, France, Russia
2. 1917
3. sank American ships
4. 1918
5. Germany and Austria

Activity 2
1. a
2. a
3. a
4. a
5. a

Activity 3
1. a
2. c
3. a
4. a
5. a

Quiz
1. true
2. false
3. true
4. true
5. true

Lesson 22

Activity 1
1. false
2. true
3. true
4. true
5. false

Activity 2
1. The Depression was not in 1829.
2. Factories were not open.
3. Banks were not open.
4. Trade between countries was not easy.
5. The President did not promise money for everyone.
6. Low tariffs did not cause economic problems.

Quiz
1. 1929
2. Franklin D. Roosevelt
3. long lines of people waiting for food
4. Roosevelt's plan to improve the lives of Americans
5. Public Works Administration

Lesson 23

Activity 1
1. Workers started labor unions.
2. There were conflicts between labor and business.
3. Workers were afraid of losing their jobs.
4. Immigrants came from Europe.
5. Immigrants worked for lower wages.
6. Workers faced many problems.
7. Workers worked by the hour or by the piece.
8. Owners cared only about making money.

Activity 2
1. b
2. a
3. a
4. b
5. b

Quiz
1. true
2. true
3. true
4. false
5. true

Lesson 24

Activity 1
1. a
2. b
3. b
4. a
5. b
6. b

Activity 2
3
5
2
6
4
1

Quiz
1. true
2. true
3. false
4. true
5. true
6. false
7. false
8. true

Lesson 25

Activity 1
2
3
4
5
1

Activity 2
1. Christopher Columbus
2. October 12
3. last Thursday in November
4. first Monday in September
5. on federal holidays

Activity 3
1. American celebrates many holidays.
2. Government offices close on federal holidays.
3. Federal employees get a day day off on federal holidays.
4. Holidays remind us of events in our history.
5. The 4th of July is Independence Day.
6. Thanksgiving Day is the last Thursday in November.

Quiz
1. true
2. false
3. false
4. false
5. false

Lesson 26

Activity 1
1. red, white, and blue
2. 13
3. stars
4. 7
5. a state
6. Oh say can you see, by the dawn's early light.
7. colonies of the U.S.

Activity 2
1. a
2. a
3. b
4. b
5. a
6. b

Quiz

2
3
4
5
1

Lesson 27

Activity 1

1. The Statue of Liberty was a gift from France.
2. France gave the Statue of Liberty in 1886.
3. The statue is a symbol of a better future to many people.
4. There is a museum on Ellis Island.
5. The Statue of Liberty holds a torch.

Activity 2

1. a
2. b
3. b
4. b
5. b

Quiz

1. France
2. Lady Liberty
3. international friendship
4. New York harbor
5. a torch

Lesson 28

Activity 1

1. The Pledge of Allegiance is a promise.
2. Americans pledge allegiance to the flag.
3. The United States is one nation.
4. Liberty and justice are for all.
5. Americans are proud of their form of government.
6. The United States is a republic.
7. In the U.S., government is by the people and for the people.
8. Americans have a democratic form of government.

Activity 2

3
4
5
6
2
1

Quiz

1. true
2. true
3. false
4. false
5. false
6. false

Lesson 29

Activity 2

1. Washington, D.C., is between Maryland and Virginia.
2. Washington, D.C., covers 67 square miles.
3. The Senate and the House meet in the Capitol.
4. The Supreme Court explains laws.
5. The White House is on Pennsylvania Avenue.
6. Washington, D.C., has many monuments.
7. There is Washington Monument in Washington, D.C.

Activity 3

1. a
2. b
3. b
4. a
5. b

Quiz

1. the President
2. 67 square miles
3. Pennsylvania Avenue
4. Maryland
5. Supreme Court Building

Lesson 30

Activity 1

1. state
2. federal
3. municipal
4. disagree with
5. counties

Activity 3

1. true
2. true
3. true
4. false
5. false
6. false

Quiz

1. c
2. b
3. b
4. a

Lesson 31

Activity 1

1. b
2. b
3. b
4. c
5. a

Activity 2

1. 1 year
2. 2½ years
3. ELA and SAW applicants
4. Special Agricultural Workers

Quiz

1. true
2. true
3. false
4. true
5. false

Lesson 32

Activity 2
1. true
2. true
3. false
4. true
5. false

Quiz
1. b
2. a
3. b
4. a
5. b

Lesson 33

Activity 1
1. a
2. b
3. b
4. a
5. a

Activity 2
1. false
2. false
3. true
4. false
5. false

Activity 3
1. Naturalized citizens can be senators.
2. There is a test for applicants for citizenship.
3. New citizens swear to be loyal and to defend the U.S.
4. Applicants for citizenship under 50 years old take a literacy test.

Quiz
1. true
2. true
3. true
4. true
5. true

Lesson 34

Activity 1
1. false
2. false
3. false
4. false
5. false

Activity 2
1. governor
2. California
3. the Bear Flag
4. north
5. 45

Quiz
1. a
2. b
3. a
4. b
5. c

Lesson 35

Activity 1
5
3
1
2
4
6

Activity 2
1. Citizens wrote the constitution of California in 1849.
2. Citizens rewrote the constitution of California in 1879.
3. The constitution of California is the highest law of the state.
4. California has 3 branches of government.
5. Senators are residents of California.
6. We elect assembly members in California every 2 years.
7. We elect senators in California every 4 years.

Quiz
1. true
2. false
3. false
4. false
5. false

Lesson 36

Activity 1
6
4
7
8
1
5
3
2

Activity 2
1. b
2. a
3. b
4. a
5. b

Quiz
1. George Herbert Bush
2. political parties
3. Democratic and Republican
4. Michael Dukakis
5. 1992